D1196603

THE AMERICA OF

GEORGE ADE

THE AMERICA OF

GEORGE ADE

(1866-1944)

Fables, Short Stories, Essays

EDITED, WITH AN INTRODUCTION BY

Jean Shepherd

G. P. PUTNAM'S SONS NEW YORK

Library of Congress Catalog Card
Number: 60-8120

MANUFACTURED IN THE UNITED STATES OF AMERICA

VAN REES PRESS • NEW YORK

CONTENTS

SHORT STORIES

MORE FABLES

ESSAYS

PREFACE

ONE NIGHT after a broadcast on which I had performed one of the lesser-known Fables by George Ade, I took a phone call which turned out to be from S. J. Perelman. He was practically in tears. We exchanged Adeisms for over an hour. It was his considered opinion that Ade was undoubtedly one of the greatest humorists, if not the most outstanding, humorist, America has yet come up with. And what's more, that it was truly sad and ridiculous that the Great Man had become merely a three-letter word meaning "Indiana Humorist" in the New York Times Sunday Crossword Puzzle. A couple of nights later at a late supper in Dinty Moore's, near Broadway, we continued what we had begun over the phone. In addition to remarking on the excellence of the blueberry cheese cake we were consuming, Perelman, in the flush of orgiastic pleasure, went on to say that he felt that Ade had influenced all of the 20th Century American humorists in one way or another and had written about blueberry pie and ice cream as no one ever had or will again.

Up to this point I had felt that Ade was a private little crotchet of my own that I had best conceal from my more literate friends, to be secretly enjoyed when no one was looking, along with other vices such as White Sox shortstops, G-8 And His Battle Aces, old movies starring Merle Oberon, and red cabbage (sweet-sour). After hearing from Sid Perelman, I began to nose around among my other colleagues in the vineyards and immediately uncovered others who lived by Ade's advice, *"Don't try to Account for Anything."* Among them is the wildly talented cartoonist-writer Shel Silverstein, who supplied me with several rare volumes of Ade to add to the present collection.

I will not pretend that putting together this volume of what I consider the best of Ade was even remotely related to work. Time and again I got hung up reading selections to my friends late at night until I'm sure they couldn't tell whether I was doing a book or getting together a vaudeville act. One more thing: since most of the material in this volume has not been reprinted since the very early days of the century, I hope that a critical reevaluation of Ade will now be possible and that later generations of Americans will not only get huge enjoyment from reading Ade, but will understand American life better by having seen it through the eyes of one of the sharpest and most realistic commentators we have ever produced.

J. S.

INTRODUCTION

D. H. LAWRENCE once observed that the American writer is obsessed with the idea of doom and futility. He singled out Melville as a good case in point and noted that Poe could only have been an American. Hemingway, Wolfe, Dos Passos, and Salinger all are marked by the same dark broodings. In spite of the comment by Dore Schary to the effect that "America is a land of happy endings . . ." we all share a secret knowledge that while happy endings are probably what everyone else will inherit, we ourselves are somehow destined for an unnameable Something at the end. Perhaps this springs from the essential loneliness of American life, which has only been aggravated by The Electronic Age and the Big Eye of TV. No one knows for certain. But we do know that almost from the very beginnings of American writing, the best documenters of the native scene have fought the battle of the lonely and the hunted. The way in which this struggle has been carried on has varied depending on the geographical environment of the individual combatant; the vastness and wildness of our continent has produced a dozen cultures or more and they all have their chroniclers, who speak with the accents of Mobile or Boston, Asheville or Chicago. But all are bound by the single theme of the individual trying to find his place in a vast maze with walls forever changing and rules that disappear before they are even understood.

Eugene Gant, Holden Caulfield, and Ahab were all blood brothers. The Great Gatsby, wandering through his Long Island parties always alone in the midst of revelry, personified The American. He was beaten by his white whale too, and Nick said about all that could be said when Gatsby's coffin was lowered into the rain-soaked American earth at a funeral no one had time to attend: "The poor son of a bitch." He might as well have been speaking of Willy Loman, who never did get that final Big Order or really learn the territory. Kerouac's Dean Moriarty, meandering off into the night lit only by the buzzing neon lights of The West Side, was fighting the same nebulous desperate war that James Jones' Private Prewitt fought and lost too. The list goes on almost endlessly, since there are 180 million American wanderers. We secretly feel that we are about to be lowered into a lonely grave unsung, to be forgotten in three weeks or three minutes. The knowledge that we are all in it together does make it easier to take, if not more understandable.

Some writers weep over the plight of man while others laugh. Many more ignore it altogether and become wealthy. It takes a particularly wide perspective and more than the usual amount of love of mankind to be able to laugh. It also involves a certain quality of detachment. And that is where George Ade and the Midwest fit into the literary battle of the individual caught in the maze.

To understand how Ade got to be Ade one has to know something of the peculiar air of the Midwest which has molded most of the American humorists from Twain to Thurber by way of Cobb and Tarkington. While the South has been drenched with Decadence, the Midwest has been swimming in a turgid sea of Futility. It is dotted with cities and towns that have never quite made it. Toledos that want to be Detroits, Detroits that want to be Chicagos, and Chicagos that forever want to be New York. And they all know they are running in a race that is fixed.

Between these major metropoli lie countless hamlets whose only ambition is to become incorporated and to beat the

County Seat at softball. In Monon, Indiana, the roar of trucks rushing toward Chicago in the night far to the north is mingled with the thunder of the trains boring through the dark bound for Cincinnati to the south. No one stops at Monon except for a load of gasoline. As fast as is humanly possible the young of the town depart for Indianapolis where they learn, in the first ten minutes after getting off the Greyhound bus, that the really live ones go to Chicago. And upon hitting Chicago there is no place to go but New York. And always, binding it all together, are the long brooding Midwestern winters and languid summers.

Spring came to my northern Indiana town when my father, coming home from work all sweaty in his dark serge winter suit, would say in the kitchen, "Let's eat fast and hop in the car and go down to The Lake and watch The Mill." Half an hour hour later we would be parked in the car looking out over the dark oily waters of Lake Michigan, with the sullen red fires of the blast furnaces and the snaky white-hot ribbons of steel in the merchant mill lighting up the sky and making all our faces look dark red and shifting black. The air was alive with spring and the fishy lake and the huge soap factory a half mile up the shore. Ten minutes down the highway the new tomato plants and spring corn lay in the dark. The old man would say "ain't that sumpin," and we would toss our ice cream sticks out the window and head for home. Lying in bed later, with the bedroom windows open to catch the breeze, the endless sounds of trains going away seemed as natural as dropping off to sleep.

The thing about the Midwest is that hardly anybody really feels part of something. Everyone is always leaving. No one ever comes except on business or to see ailing relatives. The city is too close to the farm, while beyond the last Burma Shave sign the prairie rolls flat as a tabletop endlessly to the horizon. Everywhere are evidences of faded ambitions and forlorn whistles in the dark. One newspaper loudly proclaims itself "The World's Greatest Newspaper," and they believe it. Plans go forward for the construction of "the World's First

Mile High Skyscraper." No one quite knows what will go into it. Or cares, for that matter. And all the while catfish swim in the slow coffee brown rivers and the snowball bushes line the porches in Bloomington. It is this incongruity that produces men who are compelled by secret dark inner urges to warn of the futility of the sad earthly posturing of Man. Of these there are two very common Midwestern types: the Humorist and the hellfire fundamentalist Evangelist. They both often say the same things, and for identical reasons. And, significantly enough, usually distrust each other mightily. Laughter always has been suspect, especially to the pious. While on the other hand, booming oratory, which is to the pious as rich food and nourishing (non-alcoholic) drink, is to the humorist the sound of air escaping from a balloon held by a somewhat backward but aggressive child.

Anyone who spends much time in a small midwestern community will constantly come into contact with both types of performer. Ade himself pointed out in an essay on Indiana that humorists of the nonprofessional but practicing variety can be found every few feet along Main Street. Most of them got that way out of self-protection since the spaces between them are filled with preachers. Almost all of their humor is of the school of Futility rather than the school of the Tall Tale of earlier frontier days. Futility, and the usual triumph of evil over good. Which is another name for realism.

I recall a southern Indiana man once telling me about Aunt Mary and Yaller-Eye Sparks. At the time we were fishing for bluegills in the Little Miami near the Kentucky border. I will tell it in his words: "Aunt Mary was a tall angry woman I lived with when I was a boy. She never wore anything but long Mother Hubbard dresses and had her hair done up in a bun that was as hard as a spring green apple. Well, sir, you never heard anything like her in your life. She talked in nothing but quotations from the Bible and since I was just a kid that made quite a dent in me. I could see angels in every cloud and the devil with a forked tail lived right behind the poolroom. Well in those days there was a man named Yaller-Eye Sparks who was the Town Drunk and clearly damned to hell. He was tall and handsome with a big set of walrus moustaches and he used to walk right down the middle of the road on Saturday night singing out loud to himself. Not many people did that back home. Well, I can still see Aunt Mary standing by the window watching old Yaller-Eye go past, saying in her hymn-singing voice so's I wouldn't mistake that she meant it, "There goes Yaller-Eye Sparks with the Devil in him. He is doomed! DOOMED! The devil will take him to hell before next planting!" Well, sir, Yaller-Eye and Aunt Mary were about the same age I guess. For years and years Aunt Mary kept up her prophesying and Yaller-Eye continued to drink and sing just as if he didn't know that the devil was hiding behind every bush awaiting to throw the net over him. One day she up and died of a fit after getting all riled up at the Spring Revival. She was about seventy at the time. Well, sir, Yaller-Eye lived to be 102, and was the oldest man in the county when he passed on one day after he got hit by the afternoon mail sack from off the Chicago Flyer. He never missed watching the trains go through. I remember the reporter from the county paper couldn't find him the day he come down to interview him on how come he had lived to be a hundred. Yaller-Eye was sleeping off a Saturday night under his porch at the time, and he was fit to be tied when he read in the paper the next week that he attributed his old age to Clean Living and Prayer. Plus one cigar per week. Anyway, everyone was surprised when he up and died like that, since he had been getting hit by that mail sack now and again ever since they put the Chicago Flyer on, back in the Nineties. Everyone figured he went before his time, so I guess Aunt Mary was right in the end." After which he smiled and continued to watch his bobber.

The important thing here is that these were real people. Aunt Mary and Yaller-Eye were not fiction, and what happened to them really happened. It is wise to note that the man who told the story obviously loved both of them. This is a characteristic of all true humor, and particularly of Ade's. The philosophy of Ade is a reassuring one, since everywhere there is the deep compassion of a man who has been there and seen it.

There are no heroes or noble figures in Ade. All are subject to the same trivial emotions and continual tiny frustrations, rich and poor alike. Ade, as has no one, before or since, chronicled the Great Unchronicled. Those who are totally unimportant. So profoundly insignificant that they hardly exist so far as literature is concerned. Those to whom nothing ever really happens. No tragedy or comedy. No romances or Great Loves. Those who settle for what they get and quietly move on. Which means most of us, in the end. He told better than anyone the stories of the lonely men who live out their lives in third-rate hotels and sit in lobbies watching bell boys carry bags, and whose chief reading matter is tabloid papers and blue-plate menus. Of the Agneses, who live across the street from the town belles, and who do piano finger exercises while the house across the street it all lit up. These are not the people who become dope addicts or commit suicide or even wind up pleasantly neurotic and hence characters in a play or novel. They are the Great Non-Existent. He often summed up in a phrase their whole way of life. "Once there was a lover who was on The Ragged Edge of the Desert Where Old Batchelors Live." Offhand I can't recall it being better said anywhere.

Here is another typical George Ade person, whom I've never met in any novel or play but have known intimately since I went to school with her, and have met in endless offices ever since in a dozen cities. "Once upon a Time there was a slim Girl with a Forehead which was Shiny and Protuberant, like a Bartlett Pear. When asked to put Something in an Autograph Album she invariably wrote the Following, in a tall, dislocated Back-Hand:

"Life is Real; Life is Earnest,
And the Grave is not its Goal."

That's the kind of Girl she was." Yes I know, I remember. What happened to her? You guess. But what ever did or did not happen is exactly true to life. And this is a key to Ade as well as any other true humorist. Ade always maintained that he was not a humorist but a *realist*. He reported on what he *saw* in life and not what he imagined. *The Fable of the Caddy Who Hurt His Head While Thinking* is a remarkable piece of work and a prime example of Ade at his best. Read it twice and then ask yourself why it is funny. Or is it funny at all? The third time over reads like a synopsis of *The Death of a Salesman*. The Caddy's father is right in there pitching with Willy Loman and William O. Gant. The caddy grew up to be Prewitt.

Another facet of Ade which I find fascinating is his superb reporting of the coming of Culture to Bird Center. The great shift from a farm-frontier society to the beginnings of the present homogeneous mass-urban complex that has swept over the country since the turn of the century. Since Ade lived in the primitive Indiana of the 70's and 80's as well as the roaring Chicago of the 90's and 1900's he was able to give an accurate first hand account. In his *Fables* which appeared in the old Chicago Record this theme continually reappeared and was always hilarious. Culture was usually being foisted off on the men by ambitious dreaming women. Here is a description of a typical Ade Culture-victim in a small Indiana town of the '90's:

"Once there was a Happy Family that began to get a few hard Bumps when Ma bought a Work on Etiquette. Up to that time the Outfit had not tried to throw on any Lugs. The Male Contingent slouched around the House in their Shirt-Sleeves, while the Girls often came to Breakfast in their Balloon-Wrappers, and never thought of Primping until about 3 P.M. Father had an assortment of Rube Table Manners left over from his early Experience on the Farm.

He never saw the sense of changing Knives when he hacked into the Butter, and as for using the side of the Spoon, he never could get the Hang of it.

Up to the Time that he married and became House-broke he had been a Sword-Swallower in a $4 Beanery. For years he up-ended his Soup-Plate so as to get all that was coming to him, and cooled his coffee in the Saucer, and concluded his Exhibition of Barbaric Sports by using a large limber piece of Bread as a Mop." The extreme logicality of calling a certain type of eating "one of The Barbaric Sports" is pure Ade again. And his people are true. I myself had an Uncle named Carl who was a typical Chicago Primitive. He wore false teeth that had been given him by the Relief People. This was in the Depression days and Relief was a big thing. Carl had gone on Relief as soon as he had got wind of it. It was made for him. Among other things such as canned radishes and pickled sweet potatoes, they had presented him with a set of store teeth. His cup was fairly full until a sad thing happened. One day his wife, Aunt Min by name, in a fit of pique threw the teeth down the air shaft and forever into oblivion. Carl just sat there stunned for a while, until the White Sox ball game came on the radio and took his mind off his nakedness. He never got another pair of teeth and the incident was never mentioned again in Carl's presence. But as a kid, I was always fascinated by the way he gummed his Indiana corn when he came to our house for dinner. This is a typical setback of the sort that Ade was constantly reporting. I mention it here only to show that Ade's Midwesterners were not unique nor imaginary.

Ade's life was of a sort that will never again occur in America. He was born in Kentland, Indiana in 1866. Kentland today is known only as a town where the Greyhound bus stops over for twenty minutes while the passengers stoke up on diner food before continuing on to Chicago from Indianapolis or Cincinnati to the south. In 1866 it was as isolated from the rest of the world as Antarctica. Even though Chicago was only 80 miles away it might as well have been in Europe as far as Kentland was concerned. According to records of the time there were about 600 people in Kentland, which isn't a great deal less than are living there today. His family included three boys and three girls, a normal hard-pinched father, and a mother whom Ade worshiped all of his life. One day in 1883, a day which he later celebrated in several fables, George boarded the train for Lafayette, Indiana and Purdue University, a brand new fresh-water institution, for a shot of higher education. It was at Purdue that he met John McCutcheon, who became his life-long friend and collaborator. It is not on record that Ade got much of an education at Purdue itself, but obviously Lafayette, with its theatrical road companies, vaudeville shows, and 15,000 people, was heady stuff to Ade. It taught him a lot. He became fascinated by the theatre and show people and for the rest of his life was impressed by actors and performers of all sorts. This, needless to add, is still happening to sophomores in Layfayette. The Midwesterner practically by definition is a born Audience Member. When in the outside world he feels he is eternally a guest, allowed only to participate in the proceedings because of the politeness of those around him. Or because they aren't on to him yet. In this respect Ade was a true Midwesterner. Although he was proud of his birthright he was very conscious of it and wrote numerous articles in his later days defending and explaining Indiana.

After graduation Ade remained in Lafayette in order to study law in a law office. Six weeks of this convinced Ade that he would never make it as a lawyer. The law profoundly bored him, but the experience later turned up in several excellent fables. He quit, and went to work as a reporter for a struggling Lafayette paper which shortly thereafter collapsed and died. Then came a job with a patent medicine company where he promptly made his first contribution to the language by naming a laxative "Cascarets," and coming up with a slogan for the product that is still around: "They Work While You Sleep." As with everything else he did during these days, the incident popped up in one of the fables. In 1890, the patent medicine job went the way of all jobs, so Ade packed off to Chicago where McCutcheon was working on the *Morning News* (later called the *Chicago Record*) as a cartoonist. Mc-

Cutcheon talked the editor, Charles Dennis, into giving Ade a trial and he went to work. He began by writing a daily weather report which very shortly became a popular feature of the paper. Ade was a born reporter who obviously loved his work. In addition, Chicago was an ideal town for anyone who enjoyed watching the old parade go over the cliff with all flags flying daily. And it still is. In the 90's, Chicago was a wide-open city not much different from what Nelson Algren described as "... the place built out of Man's ceaseless failure to overcome himself." Saloons and crooked aldermen, opera houses and ladies of interesting reputations, elderly boxers and packing-fortune dowagers, all were in plain sight for anyone with eyes. And if anyone ever had a pair of eyes it was George Ade. He dug in, and within a year was one of the best reporters in a town that had some good ones. His style was distinctive and began to be really noticed by readers and rival newsmen. He covered fights and elections, murders and scandals, and in short, had a pretty good opportunity to see what sort of ball game we are all playing. One of his achievements of this period was the covering of the famous Sullivan-Corbett fight in New Orleans. His accounts of this epic battle raised circulation of his paper drastically and were the talk of Chicago. In 1893 his first "Stories of the Streets and of the Town" appeared. These unsigned pieces were about anything that Ade saw, felt, or smelled, that he wanted to write about. It was a great opportunity for Ade to say a lot of things that no one else was saying. Even the Literary Set at the University of Chicago began to talk about what was happening in *The Record* every morning. The columns were illustrated by his friend McCutcheon who accompanied Ade on his daily roamings over the city looking for things to write about. Many of the pieces were written in short story form, others in an odd fictional essay style which later evolved into the *Fables.*

He experimented constantly, and the push of a daily deadline forced him to be completely unselfconscious. He wrote rapidly and rarely rewrote a line, and almost every column varied in form from the one before it. It is too bad that there are few outlets today that can give a writer such freedom and yet impose work discipline. This daily drive allowed a sort of free-swinging guttiness to come into his work of the sort which seems almost impossible to develop today.

In September of 1897 Ade turned out his first *Fable in Slang. The Fable of Sister Mae Who Did As Well As Could Be Expected* was the first of the lot. He later said that he was just sitting unsuspectingly in front of a sheet of paper when the innocent idea came to him to write something in fable form using the language and clichés of the moment. In other words, slang. He said that in order to let people know that he knew better than to use slang in writing, he decided to capitalize all suspicious words and phrases. He was mortally afraid people would think he was illiterate. In any event, *Sister Mae* did much better than Ade expected, but he had no idea of doing more fables. But talk persisted around town about his first fable, so a few months later he began to turn them out regularly. In spite of his qualms about using slang, he loved writing them. The enjoyment he got from doing them is obvious when they are read. They made such a hit locally with the *Record* readers that a Chicago publisher decided to bring out a collection to be called, logically, *Fables in Slang.*

It was issued in December of 1899, and within a short time, people all over the country were using Ade phrases and words. Practically overnight he became a national institution. William Dean Howells, the leading literary sage of the era, said, "his portrayal of life is almost absolute." To be approved by what Ade called the Serious Literary People meant a great deal to him so he was really encouraged to get to work.

Victor Lawson, the publisher of *The Record,* syndicated Ade in papers across the country after the success of the first collection of *Fables.* Late in 1900, *More Fables in Slang* appeared. It also sold enormously well and by the end of the year Ade was earning more than $1000 a week. His brother, back home, was investing his surplus cash in Indiana farmland which George felt would always be there even when the rains came. Typical of a Midwestern success, he never quite believed it had all really happened. Like Scott Fitzgerald of a generation later, he always felt he was looking through the windows at the parties he saw.

This was particularly true of his attitude toward his first Broadway success. Ever since his student days at Purdue, Ade had been a theatre addict of the most hopeless sort. He had particularly been impressed by Gilbert and Sullivan's *The Mikado* and so decided to try his hand at writing for the theatre using a form similar to Gilbert's formula. He paired up with Alfred Wathall, a musician, and began work on a musical. In those days, they were known as light operas.

The Sultan of Sula opened in New York in 1902 and was a smash hit. Ade had never seriously thought of himself as a big-time showman, but here it was. In the meantime, two more books of column material had been published, *"Artie"* and *Pink Marsh,* and now everywhere Ade was being carried around on the public's shoulders. Few writers in modern times have had so much success and general acceptance in such a short time. When *In Babel,* a collection from the old *Street and Town* column was issued, H. L. Mencken said the collection contained two or three of the very best short stories ever written in America. The story of *"Buck" and Gertie,* which touches on religious fanaticism in Michigan, was one of Mencken's all-time-favorite pieces of American writing.

With all the money that was coming in Ade built a country home on his estate near Brook, Indiana. It was an impressive English manor house which caused a sensation among the simple peasants of the area. He moved in, and within six weeks had written another item that would continue to amuse audiences for years to come. It was a play called *The College Widow,* based on life in a small Midwestern college (Wabash, to be exact). In September of 1904 it opened on Broadway and the opening was so tumultuous that Ade was forced to make a short speech between the second and third acts in order to calm the audience down so that the play could go on.

At the time there was another successful Ade play, *The County Chairman,* on Broadway, with still another about to open (*Peggy from Paris*), so it can be safely said that Ade was somewhat larger than Rodgers and Hammerstein in his day. *The College Widow* earned more than two million dollars in the years immediately following its opening and has been playing somewhere every season since. It is being seen at the current writing Off-Broadway under the title of *Leave It to Jane,* in a musical adaptation with lyrics by P. G. Wodehouse, book by Guy Bolton, and Jerome Kern's music. In the following ten years, Ade wrote several more plays and musicals that became successful by Broadway standards, but by then his prime days as a creative artist were on the wane. He continued to write for all the major magazines and an occasional collection of essays and fables was issued, but more and more his work lost its original biting freshness. There was one notable exception. In the late 20's he wrote a really delightful and excellent book of reminiscences about the saloon of pre-prohibition days entitled *The Old Time Saloon.*

Ade never married and there isn't much evidence that he ever had even a mild romance. Obviously, when he wrote *The Joys of Single Blessedness* he meant it when he said, "The Batchelor often wonders if his funeral will be an impressive occasion."

Loneliness echoes through every line of his best things, which are almost invariably about heroes whose timing is slightly off, sometimes by only five seconds, often by 2000 years. More and more he retired to his country home, Hazenden, to live as a country squire. His love for children expressed itself in huge picnics and parties which he gave on his estate for children who came to Hazenden from surrounding states. In fact, one party drew over 8000 children with accompanying parents. He was a lonely man.

In the 30's Ade quietly passed from the scene, when humor became a rough commodity to sell and tastes had changed. During the Depression, the Okies, and the Lefties that the Odets people waited for, had made laughter a thing of the past. In the days from 1866, just a year after the end of the Civil War, until the dark days of World War II, a lot of history had passed over Kentland, Indiana and Chicago both. Ade had seen it all but no longer had much to say. He died peacefully on May 16, 1944, at the age of 74, in Hazenden, almost completely unknown to millions of Americans whose language he had permanently shaped.

I remember seeing my mother one day when I was a kid. She was standing there in the kitchen with a pot in her hand, looking out of the window over the sink which was making that funny noise at the time. She was watching Brunner, our next door neighbor, stagger up his back steps with a snoot full. It was in the heart of the Depression and Brunner was on the Extra Board down at the roundhouse. He worked one day a month. It was getting on to dusk at the tail end of a bitterly cold winter day and Brunner had been celebrating his day's work. She watched him for a long time while he fumbled at the back door. Finally she said quietly, "... As the man says, 'Industry and Perseverance bring a sure Reward.'" I said "What do ya mean, Ma? What man?" She didn't answer. How could I know she was quoting George Ade? I'm not sure she knew either.

A word of advice about reading Ade. He should be taken a little at a time since his Fables were written for daily reading. His work is concentrated and pithy and is designed to be consumed like poetry, in small doses. Too much laughter is dulling and self-defeating. So restrain yourself from reading it all at one sitting. Ade has been around for sixty some odd years now without spoiling, and so can be kept a week or even longer without refrigeration.

I leave you with a word of advice from The Master:

"Avoid Crowds"

—JEAN SHEPHERD

THE AMERICA OF

GEORGE ADE

THE LEARNED PHRENOLOGIST

The Fable of the Visitor who got a Lot for Three Dollars

The Learned Phrenologist sat in his Office surrounded by his Whiskers.

Now and then he put a Forefinger to his Brow and glanced at the Mirror to make sure that he still resembled William Cullen Bryant.

Near him, on a Table, was a Pallid Head made of Plaster-of-Paris and stickily ornamented with small Labels. On the wall was a Chart showing that the Orangoutang does not have Daniel Webster's facial angle.

"Is the Graft played out?" asked the Learned Phrenologist, as he waited. "Is Science up against it or What?"

Then he heard the fall of Heavy Feet and resumed his Imitation. The Door opened and there came into the Room a tall, rangy Person with a Head in the shape of a Rocky Ford Cantaloupe.

Aroused from his Meditation, the Learned Phrenologist looked up at the Stranger as through a Glass, darkly, and pointed to a Red Plush Chair.

The Easy Mark collapsed into the Boarding-House Chair and the Man with more Whiskers than Darwin ever saw stood behind Him and ran his Fingers over his Head, Tarantula-Wise.

HUMAN BEING

"Well, well!" said the Learned Phrenologist. "Enough Benevolence here to do a family of Eight. Courage? I guess yes! Dewey's got the same kind of a Lump right over the Left Ear. Love of Home and Friends—like the ridge behind a Bunker! Firmness—out of sight! Reverence—well, when it comes to Reverence, you're certainly There with the Goods! Conscientiousness, Hope, and Ideality—the Limit! And as for Metaphysical Penetration—oh, Say, the Metaphysical Penetration, right where you part the Hair—oh, Laura! Say, you've got Charles Eliot Norton whipped to a Custard. I've got my Hand on it now. You can feel it yourself, can't you?"

"I can feel Something," replied the Human Being, with a rapt Smile.

"Wit, Compassion and Poetic Talent—right here where I've got my Thumb—a Cinch! I think you'll run as high as 98 per cent on all the Intellectual Faculties. In your Case we have a Rare Combination of Executive Ability, or the Power to Command, and those Qualities of Benevolence and Ideality which contribute to the fostering of Permanent Religious Sentiment. I don't know what your present Occupation is, but you ought to be President of a Theological Seminary. Kindly slip me Three Dollars before you Pass Out."

The Tall Man separated himself from Two Days' Pay and then went out on the Street and pushed People off the Sidewalk, He thought so well of Himself.

Thereafter, as before, he drove a Truck, but he was always glad to know that he could have been President of a Theological Seminary.

Moral: *A good Jolly is worth Whatever you Pay for it.*

The Fable of The Boston Biologist & The Native with the Blue Hardware

Down in the Ague Belt there was a town called Miasma. It needed Paint, Sidewalks, Tooth-Brushes and Bibles.

Everybody in Miasma believed that the Sun rose just in the edge of Widow Clevison's Hog Lot and set over on yon side of the Sand Ridge. While the Residents were Standing around on the warm side of the General Store so as to get shut of the Daily Chill they would feel sorry for Folks who had to put up with Brooklyn and Old Point Comfort.

Now it happened that a Boston Biologist had been in those Parts collecting Amphibious Fauna. The Natives called them Varmints and Sarpentile Insects.

One Day the Biologist sat on a long-waisted Truck at the Station Platform and waited for the Train that was to carry him to some Place where he could get Beans properly cooked. He had his Satchel between his Legs and was reading the Numbers on the Freight Cars in order to entertain himself.

Presently a Native appeared and walked back and forth in front of the Boston Man. The Native had a Saffron Complexion and wore high-heeled Boots. Every time he stepped there was a muffled Castinet Effect caused by the Quinine Pellets. Every one in Miasma took Quinine, except the Boston Biologist and he took Quin-een.

The Native wore on and about his Person and somewhat exposed to View a 48-Calibre Shooting-Iron, a Bowie Knife large enough for spading the Garden and several rows of Cartridges.

"I reckon we've got the purest Climate and the noblest People on God's Green Footstool," remarked the Native, pausing in front of the Biologist. "Don't say different or I may have to Gallop right through you."

"Life is very sweet to me," said the Boston Man. "I am just getting my Golf Score below 120. So I will not Contradict you. Only, I would like to ask."

"Come on with it," said the Native.

"I would like to ask, who held you while they strapped all those Chatelaine Effects on you?"

"I wear these Weepins in order to protect my Honor," replied Mr. Janders, for such was his name.

"Your Honor must be hard pushed if you have to tote such an Extensive Kit with which to defend it," observed the Boston Man.

"Well, I've got a Reputation that reaches up and down the Road," said Mr. Janders. "I've never been Curried below the Knees. I'm Long and Woolly. I've got seven or eight Fiery Nostrils and holes bored for more. I'm Pizen Ivy and can't be handled. I hate to talk about myself, but I must say I'm a Brave Little Man."

At that Moment the Train pulled in and the Boston Biologist hurried aboard, resuming the Conversation as he leaned out from the open Window of the Car.

"You say you are a Brave Man?" he asked.

"You heerd me," replied the Native, picking his Teeth with the Bowie.

"What is your Definition of a Brave Man?" asked the Biologist.

"A Brave Man is one who is not afeerd to Die," answered Mr. Janders.

"Therefore I judge that you are not afraid to depart from Miasma and take your Chances," said the Biologist. "How long have you lived here?"

"Twenty-seven Years," was the Reply.

The Boston Man looked across the Street at the dun-colored Hotel propped up by a comatose Livery Stable. Near at hand was a Pool of Green Water within which the Bacilli were croaking loudly. The Sky-Line was a row of red clay Hills pin-feathered with Saplings. A brackish Odor of Moonshine Whiskey tingled in the warm Air, and over the whole dejected Landscape lay a soft Pall of the real, Simon-Pure Malaria—the kind that can be put up in Tins and sent from Place to Place.

"You have lived here twenty-seven Years and you are not afraid to Die," said the Boston Man, reflectively. "I don't blame you. If I had lived here for twenty-seven Years I would not be afraid to Die, either. In fact, I think I'd be downright Anxious to Die."

But the crafty Biologist did not release this Body Blow until he was good and sure that the Train had started to move.

The infuriated Native had to take his chances with a Moving Target, so instead of plunking the Man from Boston, he made a Wing Shot on a State Senator who was riding on a Pass.

Still, it was taking an Awful Chance.

Moral: *Home is where the Heart is.*

The Fable of The Bureau of Public Comfort & The Man in Charge

The Druggist stood in his Place of Business surrounded by Capsules, Hot Water Bags, Perfumes and Fluid Extracts. A Man came in and said he wanted to look at the Directory. Then he asked if "Murphy" was spelled with an "f." He looked at the Hair Brushes, whistled a few bars of the "Spring Song" and went out.

A Small Boy entered and wanted to trade two empty Bottles for a Piece of Licorice Root. The Deal fell through, because the Bottles had a Name blown in the Glass.

A Woman came in and said she was waiting for a Friend. She had the Druggist bring her a Glass of Plain Water. She said she could not drink Soda Water because the Gas got up her Nose.

Another Woman came in for a Stamp. She did not have any Change with her, but was going to come in and hand him the Two Cents some time; that is, if he was Small enough to remember it.

The next who came in was a Man with hardly any Chin. He wanted a Free Sample of Liver Pills and an Almanac telling the Date of the Battle of New Orleans, when the Sun rises and sets and why the Chicken crossed the Road.

After him there came a Man who was in a Hurry and wanted to use the 'Phone. He was vexed when he learned that Skinner & Skinner did not have any Number. He asked the Druggist why it was. The Druggist said he was sorry and would See to it before the Man came in again.

Soon after two little Girls came on a Run and helped themselves to Picture Cards. They left the Door open, and a Boy in Overalls stepped in to ask if he could hang a Lithograph in the Window. The Druggist went back into the Laboratory and got a large stone Pestle. He was just ready to beat the Life out of the Cash Register when an Elderly Gentleman came in with a Prescription.

The Druggist Stayed the Blow and chirked up quite a bit. "This is where I catch even on the Day," he said.

It was no Mirage. He had to and he did.

Moral: *Don't Blame the Druggist.*

The Fable of the Good Fellow Who Got the Short End of It

Living in a Country Town there was a Boy who was Easy. When the Gang went fishing they took Him along to carry the Bait, and when they went Swimming in the Deep Hole, he had to stay on the Bank and watch their Clothes.

His Right Name was Melford Praxiteles Johnson, but he was so good-natured that everybody saluted him as Mel.

Sometimes he would go out to the Commons, where the Boys were playing Two-Old-Cat, and they would have him act as Back-Stop and chase the Flies. Somebody had to do it, and he was so Accommodating and Friendly he did it rather than delay the Game.

All the little bull-headed boys, who threatened to take their Bats and go home unless they could have their own way, played the Star Positions.

When he was a little older he went to a Medical School, where he was promptly tossed up in a Blanket and then dropped down an Air-Shaft, because the Hazers saw that he was a Good Fellow and would not go and Squeal to the Faculty.

Mel was a Bright Student, and graduated at the Head of his Class. He won a Set of Instruments for his Thesis on the Osteology of the Supernumerary Digits, and the Dean predicted Great Things for him.

He hung out a Shingle right across the Street from a Classmate who had finished at the Tail End, and did not know the difference between the Duodenum and the Clavicle. But this Classmate grew Whiskers and wore a Prince Albert and a Tall Hat and Glasses with a Gold Chain and Coughed into his Palm and used Latin Words, and he got the Practice.

He was a Physician and Mel was Doc.

If a Man came into Mel's Office, suffering from a Combination of Soft-Shell Crabs and Neapolitan Pudding, it would be like Mel to tell him that he had the Stomach-Ache.

Then the dissatisfied Patient would go across to see the Physician, who would tell him that he had Acute Gastritis.

Anybody would rather have Gastritis than Stomach-Ache, so the Physician had his Waiting-Room crowded all the Time.

The Public could not pin its Faith to a Practitioner who wore a Sack Suit and kept his Hat on the Back of his Head and spoke to the Children along the Street, and never used Double-Jointed Words from the Materia Medica unless he had to.

Still Doc managed to get some Practice. If any Sufferer happened to be Broke, he went to Doc, because Doc was a Good Fellow, who could be Stood Off. Doc got all the

Charity cases and the Fake across the Street treated all the Women who had Property and Imaginary Complaints.

Shortly after Doc began to Practice, he fell in Love, but no one took it Seriously. The Girl liked Doc because he was entertaining and liberal, up to his Income, but when he Proposed, his Sense of Humor prevented him from getting down on his Knees and giving her any of this Mrs. E. D. E. N. Southworth Hanky-Pank.

She had the usual streak of the Romantic in her Make-Up, and she refused to consider his offhand Request. She gave herself to an opinionated Willie-Boy who was always having himself Photographed in a Dress Suit, and who came at her with a Ten-Minute Speech that he had learned from a Book on "How to Make Love," published by Munro & Co.

Then because Doc's Philosophy and his Goodness of Heart came to his Rescue and he Forgave her and did not Drink himself to Death or start for the Gold Fields with her Picture next to his Heart, nearly every one said that he had not Cared for her at all and was not capable of the Grand Passion.

After Doc had struggled along in his Profession for many Years without having any Velvet in front of him, he decided to try for a Political Appointment. Every one seemed to like him and he knew he could get Backing. He thought very well of his Drag. Sure enough, when he applied for a Consulate, all the influential Moguls of the Party signed his Petition. Then they sat down and wrote Private Letters to Back-Cap him.

They told the President that he was a Good Fellow, but he lacked Dignity and Bearing. They said that he was commonly known as Mel or Doc, that he had a Reputation as a Story-Teller, that he had been a Failure in his Profession, and never accumulated any Property, that he was Careless in his Business Habits and loaned Money to any one who seemed to be in Trouble, and that, therefore, although he had been an Active Worker, possibly the Appointment ought to go to some Man who had more regard for Solemn Responsibilities.

So the Job was given to a Four-Flush who posed in Public Places and Frowned and kept one Hand inside of his Coat and never said anything because he had Nothing to say.

Even after this final Throw-Down Doc did not become embittered or cease trying to be a Good Fellow.

One Day, however, as he was reviewing his Career, he decided that if he had it to do over again, he would be M. Praxiteles Johnson and wear the Front of Jove.

He realized that he had Erred in trying to be a Mixer. He wished that he had kept his Degree printed on all his Cards and hung an Articulated Skeleton inside of his Office Door. Also, he began to understand that it is advisable to crowd in on the Platform at every public Pow-wow and be played up as a Prominent Citizen. Furthermore, he wished that he had Dressed the same as an Undertaker.

It would have been a Hard Job to keep up the Monumental Bluff, but then one must always pay a price for True Success.

Moral: *Be Dignified and Serious, if possible.*

The Fable of Springfield's Fairest Flower and Lonesome Agnes Who Was Crafty

Springfield had a Girl who was being Courted by a Syndicate. She was the Girl who took First Prize at the Business Men's Carnival. When the Sunday Paper ran a whole Page of Typical Belles she had the Place of Honor.

If a Stranger from some larger Town was there on a Visit and it became necessary to Knock his Eye out and prove to him that Springfield was strictly In It, they took him up to call on Mazie. Mazie never failed to Bowl him over, for she was a Dream of Loveliness when she got into her Glad Raiment. Mazie had large mesmeric Eyes and a

Complexion that was like Chaste Marble kissed by the Rosy Flush of Dawn. She carried plenty of Brown Hair that she Built Up by putting Rats under it. When she sat very straight on the edge of the Chair, with the queenly Tilt of the Chin and the Shoulders set back Proudly and the Skirt sort of Whipped Under so as to help the General Outline, she was certainly a Pleasing Object to size up. She did not Fall Down on any Point.

Mazie had such a Rush of Men Callers that the S. R. O. Sign was out almost every Night, and when the Weather permitted she had Overflow Meetings on the Veranda.

Right across the Street from Beautiful Mazie there lived a Girl named Agnes, who was Fair to Middling, although she could not Step it Off within twenty Seconds of Mazie's regular Gait. Sometimes when she happened to get the right Combination of Colors and wore a Veil and you did not get too Close, she was not Half Bad, but as soon as she got into the same Picture with Mazie, the Man Charmer, she was faded to a Gray Bleach.

All the plain, everyday XX Springfield Girls, designed for Family Use and not for Exhibition Purposes, used to wish that Mazie would go away somewhere and forget to come back.

The Other Girls had to Admit that Mazie was a good deal of a Tangerine, but they did not Enthuse the same as their Brothers did. You cannot expect a lot of Spirited Girls to strike a Chord in G and sing any Anthem of Praise to a Friend who is trying to make Wall Flowers of them. When some Poor Man who was off his Dip on Matchless Mazie, the Sprite of Springfield, would start a Rhapsody to some other Girl, the Other Girl would say Yes, that Mazie was a Sweet and Lovely Girl, but when she said it she would look as if she had just tasted a Lemon.

But Agnes, who lived across the Street from the Pearl of Springfield, tried to be Cheerful and Keep her Hammer hidden, although goodness knows she had Reason to feel Put Out. It is Hard Lines for a Sociable Girl to sit around the House and practise Finger movements on the Piano and see everything Lighted Up across the Street.

Agnes felt sometimes as if she would just have to Up and Tell the Boys what a deceitful, two-faced old Thing this Mazie really was. But she knew better than to do it, for Mazie had all of them Zizzy and they would have said that Agnes was Miffed because of Mazie's Popularity.

Agnes understood that Men always show a Strong Preference for a Feather Headed Girl, if she has the Looks and a Circus Style, and particularly if all the sedate, well read, plain, intellectual Girls are trying to Close Up ahead of her, so as to throw her into a Pocket.

So long as Mazie was the Reigning Fad, and while Mazie's Front Room was the Mecca for Golf Players and Glee Club Undergraduates, Agnes sat back, a trifle Forlorn, but not so Rattled that she took any Chances of Queering her own Game.

Sometimes when there was such a Push at Mazie's Home that the Late Comers could not get up to within Rubbering Distance of the celebrated Siren of Springfield, and it was too Early to go Home, one or two of the Young Men would drift over to pay a little Attention to Agnes. Here was the chance for Agnes to make the Mistake of her Life. But she never asked them if they had been to see Mazie first, and she never made any of these unwelcome Cracks about being Second Choice. She received them with the long Hand Clasp and the Friendly Smile, and threw herself to Entertain them, wotting well that now and then a Girl must pocket her Pride and she Laughs Best who postpones her Laughing until after the Banns have been Published.

Instead of seeking to undermine the Uncrowned Queen of Springfield and put the Skids under her, she lauded Mazie to the Skies. She asked the Boys if they did not think that Mazie was a Dashing Beauty and by far the Swellest in Town, and was it any Wonder that the whole Crowd was Dotty about her. When she talked like that, Beaux who had been getting the gleaming Cold Shoulder from Mazie, were inclined to Demur and say that Mazie was unquestionably an Artist on the Make-up and a Caution when it came to Coquettish Wiles, but there were Others just as Nice.

In this Town of Springfield there was a Steady Young Fellow who wrote Junior after his Name, and was Prospective Heir to an Iron Foundry. He was Foolish about Mazie for quite a Spell, but when he went up to see her and try to make it worth her Time to look him over, the Door-Bell kept ringing, and he found that instead of conducting a Courtship he was simply getting in on a Series of Mass Meetings. So he dropped out of the Competition and took to calling on Agnes, and found that he was the Whole Thing. She treated him Kindly and never disagreed with him except on one Point. Whenever he would say that Mazie was getting the Big Head and put on too many Frills to suit him, and had been Spoiled by having so many on her Staff at one time, Agnes would stick up for her Friend, and say that she could hardly blame any Man for giving in to the Superlative Charms of One who had Julia Marlowe set back a Mile.

She kept that Talk going until he was good and tired of having Mazie dingdonged at him. One Evening he stopped her right in the middle of an Eulogium and suggested that they let up on the Mazie Topic and talk about Themselves for a while. And although she Protested, he convinced her that she was worth a Ten Acre Field full of Mazies.

So they were Married and went to Niagara Falls and came Home and still Mazie remained Single.

She was supposed to be several Notches too High Up for any One Man in Springfield. After getting such Job Lots of Adulation and having at least six pulsating Courtiers kneeling on her Sofa Pillows every Evening it would have been a Tame Let-Down for her to splice up with one lone Business Man and settle down to a dull Existence in some Apartment House.

So it came about that there was a General Impression in Springfield that Mazie was the Unattainable. She was a kind of Public Character to be Idolized, but not removed from the Pedestal. The discouraged Suitors fell away one by one, and married the ordinary Girls who were willing to Play Fair and not keep the Applicants dangling. Mazie took up with a new Generation and seemed to believe that she could reign Forever, the same as the Elfin Queen in the Fairy Tale.

But the Peach Crops come and go.

After a few Years Mazie's Door-Bell did not Tinkle with its whilom frequency, and right down the Street there was a Seventeen-Year-Older who had shot up out of Short Dresses like a Willow Sprout, and it was her Picture that went into the Special Illustrated Edition as Springfield's Fairest Daughter.

Mazie saw that the Vernal Season had passed and the Harvest Time was at Hand, so she decided to chop the Philandering and pick one for Keeps. But when she began to encourage the Eligibles they took it to mean that she was prolonging the same old String Game. The Men who knew that she had turned down at least Fifty figured that there was no Possible Chance for them, so they were Leery and would not be led into Committing themselves. Besides, Mazie had been handed around by so many that she was beginning to be Graded as Second Hand, and there was not the same keen Anxiety to capture her that there had been along about the Year of the World's Fair.

At last Accounts she was supposed to be Guessing. Agnes is doing Nicely, with a well trained Husband.

Moral: *Cheer Up, Girls.*

The Fable of the Wise Piker Who Had the Kind of Talk That Went

Once there was a man who wore a Six Hat and had a Head shaped like an Egg Plant. He had not found time to sit down and absorb Culture. Yet he had to go out and meet the high Mansard Foreheads. Sometimes he found himself in the Front Room where every one was expected to discuss Literature, Art, Music and the Difficulty of getting good Kitchen Help.

This Man was a Pin-Head in a good many Respects, but he was Wise as a Serpent.

This Man was what Edmund Clarence Stedman would call a Piker. A Piker is one who gets into the Game on Small Capital and Lets On to be holding back a huge Reserve. A Piker is usually Safe when he sagatiates among the Well-Bred because they are too Polite to call a Bluff.

A Piker always has his entire Stock of Goods in the Show Window.

When it came to Music, the Piker did not know the difference between a Fugue and a Cantata. Such knowledge of Literature as he could boast was picked up by reading the Posters in front of Book-Stores. The average Katy-Did had about as much Art Education as he could have Spread had it come to a Show-Down. He had as much Business in an Assemblage of cultivated Chautauquans as a man with a ragged $2.00 Bill would have in Wall Street. Yet he managed to cut Figure Eights over the Thin Ice and he had the name of being one of the Brainiest Gentlemen that ever accepted an Invitation to the Evening Session of the Olympian Circle of Hens.

The Piker knew the Value of the Stock Phrase. And the way he could raise a Dust and dodge out of a Tight Place was a little Bit of All Right.

One evening the Piker went to call on Mrs. Hester Kazam, author of many unpublished Poems, and the boss Diana of the Tuft-Hunters. At the Kazam Home, which is rigged up with Red Blankets and Green Lamps so as to be Oriental, he bumped into Henrietta Hunter Haw, who will be remembered as the Young Lady who poured at the Afternoon Reception to F. Hopkinson Smith.

Miss Haw reclined at half length in the Turkish Corner and asked the Piker what he thought of Sienkiewicz. The

Piker knew that he had heard that name sprung somewhere before, but if he had tried to Pronounce it, he would have gone to the Floor. He didn't know whether Sienkiewicz was the author of "Lovers Once but Strangers Now" or "The Gentleman from Arkansaw." However, he was not to be Feazed. He knew the kind of Conversational Parsley that is needed to Garnish a full-blown Intellectual Vacuum, and he passed some of it to Henrietta.

He said he liked Sienk, so far as the Psychological Analysis was concerned, but it sometimes occurred to him that there was a lack of Insight and Broad Artistic Grasp.

That is the Style of Vapor calculated to keep a Young Woman anchored right in the Turkish Corner and make her believe she has met the Really and Truly Gazip.

The Piker unreeled a little more of the same kind. He said that the Elaboration of Incident showed a certain Modicum of Skill, but there was not enough Plus-Human Sympathy in the Coloring of the Subtle Motives. When the Piker got rid of this he was always Relieved, for it is an Awful Thing to Memorize and carry around with you.

Afterward Miss Haw went out and told her Girl Friends that the Piker was Terrible Deep.

When they brought up Music, that was where the Piker lived. He could get in early and stay late and never Trip himself up. He had attended a couple of Concerts and at one time boarded with a Lady who played the Autoharp.

One Evening when he was out with a few People who were such Thorough Musicians that they seemed Sour about something all the time, a Tall Man with a Low Collar asked him if he had heard that latest Thing by Tschaikowsky.

If he had made it Charles K. Harris, the Piker might have been with him. But he never turned a Hair.

"Impressive, isn't it!" he said, having learned how to Spar for Wind, without leaving an Opening.

"Yes, but it didn't get into me the way Vogner does," replied the Tall Party.

This was the Cue for the Piker to insert his Speech on Vogner.

He said he preferred Vogner any day in the Week on account of the distinct Appeal to the Intellectual Side and the Atmosphere of Mysticism, whatever that was. He said he couldn't listen to Vogner without going into a Cold Sweat and Chewing the Buttons off his Gloves, particularly if the Interpretation was made with a Broad and Comprehensive Virtuosity and such Mastery of Technique as to abolish all suggestion of the Intermediary and bring one into direct Communion with the Soul-Moods.

Then the Tall Man would know just as much about it as the Piker did.

Among the Acquaintances was a Lady named Wigley, who was Crazy about Art. In her Parlor she had one of her own Works entitled "Sunset on the Little Miami River," with a Frame that cost $26.00. It was Miss Wigley who read the Paper before the Raphael Suburbanites, setting forth that the Highest Effects could not be obtained by the Use of Crayon. She loved to hear the Piker cut loose about Art. Even when he got in over his Head, she was right there swimming along after him and never missing a Stroke.

Mrs. Wigley was stuck on his Conversation because he said so many things that could be Thought About later on. Nearly every one who heard him went Home and Thought about what he had said and Wondered what he had been Driving at.

Mrs. Wigley had a Theory that an Artist who is any Good at all should be able to suggest through the Medium of Colors all that he or she felt and suffered during the Throes of Execution. So she called in the Piker to size up her Picture of the Little Miami River at Sundown and asked him what Emotion, if any, was stirred up within him as he gazed at the Effort. The Piker said it gave him a touch of Sadness. Then she knew he was a real Critic all right.

The Piker kept it up until after a while he began to think that possibly he was something of a Sassy Savant.

He was elected Director of a Museum and was invited to sit on the Platform at Lectures. And at last he departed this Life, with only a few Relatives and Intimate Friends being on to him.

Moral: *For Parlor Use the Vague Generality is a Life-Saver.*

The Fable of the Slim Girl who Tried to Keep a Date that was Never Made

Once upon a Time there was a slim Girl with a Forehead which was Shiny and Protuberant, like a Bartlett Pear. When asked to put Something in an Autograph Album she invariably wrote the Following, in a tall, dislocated Back-Hand:

"Life is Real; Life is Earnest,
And the Grave is not its Goal."

That's the kind of a Girl she was.

In her own Town she had the Name of being a Cold Proposition, but that was because the Primitive Yokels of a One-Night Stand could not Attune Themselves to the Views of one who was troubled with Ideals. Her Soul Panted for the Higher Iife.

Alas, the Rube Town in which she Hung Forth was given over to Croquet, Mush and Milk Sociables, a lodge of Elks and two married Preachers who doctored for the Tonsilitis. So what could the Poor Girl do?

In all the Country around there was not a Man who came up to her Plans and Specifications for a Husband. Neither was there any Man who had any time for Her. So she led a lonely Life, dreaming of the One—the Ideal. He was a big and pensive Literary Man, wearing a Prince Albert coat, a neat Derby Hat and godlike Whiskers. When He came he would enfold Her in his Arms and whisper Emerson's Essays to her.

COLD PROPOSITION

But the Party failed to show up.

Often enough she put on her Chip Hat and her Black Lisle Gloves and Sauntered down to look at the Gang sitting in front of the Occidental Hotel, hoping that the Real Thing would be there. But she always saw the same old line of Four-Flush Drummers from Chicago and St. Louis, smoking Horrid Cigars and talking about the Percentages of the League Teams.

She knew that these Gross Creatures were not prone to chase mere Intellectual Splendor, so she made no effort to Flag them.

When she was Thirty-Four years of age and was able to

FOUR-FLUSH DRUMMER

recite "Lucile" without looking at the Book she was Married to a Janitor of the name of Ernest. He had been kicked in the Head by a Mule when young and believed everything he read in the Sunday Papers. His pay was Twenty-Three a month, which was high, if you knew Ernest.

His Wife wore a red Mother Hubbard all during the Remainder of her Life.

This is invariably a Sign of Blasted Hopes.

Moral: *Never Live in a Jay Town.*

NEW YORK MAN

The Fable of the New York Person Who Gave the Stage Fright to Fostoria, Ohio

A New York man went to visit a Cousin in the Far West. The name of the Town was Fostoria, Ohio.

When he came into Town he had his Watch-Chain on the outside of his Coat, and his Pink Spats were the first ever seen in Fostoria.

"Have you a Manicure Parlor in this Beastly Hole?" asked the New York Man, as they walked up from the Train.

"What's that?" asked the Cousin, stepping on his own Feet.

"Great Heavens!" exclaimed the New York Man, and was silent for several Moments.

At Dinner he called for Artichokes, and when told that there were none, he said, "Oh, very well," in a Tone of Chastened Resignation.

After Dinner he took the Family into the Parlor, and told the Members how much they would Enjoy going to Weber and Fields'. Seeing a Book on the Table, he sauntered up to It and said, "Ah, one of Dick Davis' Things." Later in the Evening he visited the only Club House in Town. The Local Editor of the Evening Paper was playing Pin-Pool with the Superintendent of the Trolley Line. When the New York Man came into the Room, they began to Tremble and fell down on their Shots.

The Manager of the Hub and Spoke Factory then asked the New York Man to have a Drink. The New York Man wondered if a Small Bottle was already cold. They said Yes, but it was a Lie, The Boy had to go out for it.

He found One that had been in the Window of the Turf Exchange since the Grand Opening, the Year after Natural Gas was discovered. The New York Man drank it, remarking that it was hardly as Dry as he usually got it at Martin's.

The Club Members looked at Him and said Nothing. They thought he meant Bradley-Martin's.

Next Day the New York Man was Interviewed by the Local Editor. In the Evening he attended the Annual Dinner of the Bicycle Club, and went Home early because the Man sitting next to him put Ice in his Claret.

In due time he returned to New York, and Fostoria took off its White Shirt.

Some Weeks after that, the Cousin of the New York Man had an Opportunity to visit the Metropolis. He rode on an Extra Ticket with a Stockman who was shipping three Car-Load of Horses, and got a Free Ticket for every Car-Load.

When the Cousin arrived at New York he went to the address, and found the New York Man at Dinner.

SNAKE CHARMER

There was a Sheaf of Celery on the Table.

Opposite the New York Man sat a Chiropodist who drank.

At his right was a Large Woman in a Flowered Wrapper—she had been Weeping.

At his left was a Snake-Charmer from Huber's Museum.

The New York Man asked the Cousin to wait Outside, and then explained that he was stopping there Temporarily. That Evening they went to Proctor's, and stood during the Performance.

Moral: *A New York Man never begins to Cut Ice until he is west of Rahway.*

The Fable of the Good Fairy with the Lorgnette, and why She Got it Good

Once Upon a Time there was a Broad Girl who had nothing else to do and no Children to look after, so she thought she would be Benevolent.

She had scared all the Red Corpuscles out of the 2 by 4 Midget who rotated about her in a Limited Orbit and was known by Courtesy as her Husband. He was Soft for her, and so she got it Mapped out with Herself that she was a Superior Woman.

She knew that when she switched the Current on to

THE MIDGET

herself she Used up about 6,000 Ohms an hour, and the whole Neighborhood had to put on Blinders.

She had read about nine Subscription Books with Cupid and Dove Tail-Pieces and she believed that she could get away with any Topic that was batted up to her and then slam it over to Second in time to head off the Runner.

Her clothes were full of Pin-Holes where she had been hanging Medals on Herself, and she used to go in a Hand-Ball Court every Day and throw up Bouquets, letting them bounce back and hit Her.

Also, She would square off in front of a Camera every Two Weeks, and the Man was Next, for he always removed the Mole when he was touching up the Negative. In the Photograph the Broad Girl resembled Pauline Hall, but outside of the Photograph, and take it in the Morning when she showed up on the Level, she looked like a Street just before they put on the Asphalt.

But never you Fear, She thought She had Julia Arthur and Mary Mannering Seventeen up and One to play, so far as Good Looks were concerned; and when it came to the Grey Matter—the Cerebrum, the Cerebellum, and the Medulla Oblongata—May Wright Sewall was back of the Flag and Pulled up Lame.

The Down-Trodden Man, whom she had dragged to the Altar, sized Her all right, but he was afraid of his Life. He wasn't Strong enough to push Her in front of a Cable Car, and he didn't have the Nerve to get a Divorce. So he stood for Everything; but in the Summer, when She skated off into the Woods to hear a man with a Black Alpaca Coat lecture to the High Foreheads about the Subverted Ego, he used to go out with a few Friends and tell them his Troubles and weep into his Beer. They would slap him on the Back and tell him she was a Nice Woman; but he knew better.

Annyhow, as Bobby Gaylor used to say, she became restless around the House, with nothing to do except her Husband, so she made up her mind to be Benevolent to beat the Band. She decided that she would allow the Glory of her Presence to burst upon the Poor and the Uncultured. It would be a Big Help to the Poor and Uncultured to see what a Real Razmataz Lady was like.

She didn't Propose to put on Old Clothes, and go and live with Poor People, and be One of Them, and nurse their Sick, as they do in Settlements. Not on Your Previous Existence! She was going to be Benevolent, and be Dead Swell at the Same Time.

Accordingly, she would Lace Herself until she was the shape of a Bass Viol, and put on her Tailor-Made, and the Hat that made her Face seem longer, and then she would

THE BROAD GIRL

Gallop forth to do Things to the Poor. She always carried a 99-cent Lorgnette in one Hand and a Smelling-Bottle in the Other.

"Now," she would say, feeling Behind to make sure that she was all strung up, "Now, to carry Sunshine into the Lowly Places."

As soon as she struck the Plank Walks, and began stalking her prey, the small Children would crawl under the Beds, while Mother would dry her Arms on the Apron, and murmur, "Glory Be!" They knew how to stand off the Rent-Man and the Dog-Catcher; but when 235 pounds of Sunshine came wafting up the Street, they felt that they were up against a New Game.

The Benevolent Lady would go into a House numbered 1135A with a Marking Brush, and after she had sized up the front room through the Lorgnette, she would say: "My Good Woman, does your Husband drink?"

"Oh, yes, sir," the grateful Woman would reply. "That is, when he's working. He gets a Dollar Ten."

"And what does he do with all his Money?" the Benevolent Lady would ask.

" I think he plays the Stock Market," would be the Reply.

Then the Benevolent Lady would say: "When the Unfortunate Man comes Home this Evening you tell him that a Kind and Beautiful Lady called and asked him please to stop Drinking, except a Glass of Claret at Dinner, and to be sure and read Eight or Ten Pages from the Encyclopædia Britannica each night before retiring; also tell him to be sure and save his Money. Is that your Child under the Bed?"

"That's little William J."

"How Many have you?"

"Eight or Nine—I forget Which."

"Be sure and dress them in Sanitary Underwear; you can get it for Four Dollars a Suit. Will you be good enough to have the Little Boy come from under the Bed, and spell 'Ibex' for the Sweet Lady?"

"He's afraid of you."

"Kindly explain to him that I take an Interest in him, even though he is the Offspring of an Obscure and Ignorant Workingman, while I am probably the Grandest Thing that ever Swept up the Boulevard. I must go now, but I will Return. Next time I come I hope to hear that your Husband has stopped Drinking and is very Happy. Tell the Small Person under the Bed that if he learns to spell 'Ibex' by the time I call again I will let him look at my Rings. As for you, bear in mind that it is no Disgrace to be Poor; it is simply Inconvenient, that's all."

Having delivered herself of these Helpful Remarks she would Duck, and the Uplifted Mother would put a Nickel in the Can and send Lizzie over to the Dutchman's.

In this manner the Benevolent Lady carried forward the Good Work, and Dazzled the whole Region between O'Hara's Box Factory and the City Dump. It didn't Cost anything, and she derived much Joy from the Knowledge that Hundreds of People were Rubbering at her, and remarking in Choked Whispers: "Say, ain't she the Smooth Article?"

But one day a Scrappy Kid, whose Mother didn't have any Lorgnette or Diamond Ear-Bobs, spotted the Benevolent Lady. The Benevolent Lady had been in the House telling his Mother that it was a Glorious Privilege to wash for a Living.

After the Benevolent Lady went away the Kid's Mother sat down and had a Good Cry, and the Scrappy Kid thought it was up to him. He went out to the Alley and found a Tomato Can that was not working, and he waited.

In a little while the Benevolent Lady came out of a Basement, in which she had been telling a Polish Family to look at her and be Happy. The Scrappy Kid let drive, and the Tomato Can struck the Benevolent Lady between the Shoulder Blades. She squawked and started to run, fell over a Garbage Box, and had to be picked up by a Policeman.

She went Home in a Cab, and told her Husband that the Liquor League had tried to Assassinate her, because she was Reforming so many Drunkards. That settled it with her—

she said she wouldn't try to be Benevolent any more—so she joined an Ibsen Club.

The Scrappy Kid grew up to be a Corrupt Alderman, and gave his Mother plenty of Good Clothes, which she was always afraid to wear.

Moral: *In uplifting, get underneath.*

The Fable of the Kid who Shifted his Ideal

An A. D. T. Kid carrying a Death Message marked "Rush" stopped in front of a Show Window containing a Picture of James J. Jeffries and began to weep bitterly.

A kind-hearted Suburbanite happened to be passing along on his Way to the 5:42 Train. He was carrying a Dog Collar, a Sickle, a Basket of Egg Plums and a Bicycle Tire.

The Suburbanite saw the A. D. T. Kid in Tears and it struck him that here was a Bully Chance to act out the Kind-Hearted Pedestrian who is always played up strong in the Sunday School Stories about Ralph and Edgar.

"Why do you weep?" he asked, peering at the Boy through his concavo-convex Nose Glasses.

"Oh, gee! I was just Thinking," replied the Urchin, brokenly. "I was just Thinking what chance have I got to grow up and be the Main Stem, like Mr. Jeffries."

"What a perverted Ambition!" exclaimed the Suburbanite. "Why do you set up Mr. Jeffries as an Ideal? Why do you not strive to be like Me? Is it not worth a Life of Endeavor to command the Love and Respect of a Moral Settlement on the Outskirts? All the Conductors on our Division speak pleasantly to Me, and the Gateman has come to know my Name. Last year I had my Half-Tone in the Village Weekly for the mere Cost of the Engraving. When we opened Locust avenue from the Cemetery west to Alexander's Dairy, was I not a Member of the Committee

THE KID

appointed to present the Petition to the Councilmen? That's what I was! For Six Years I have been a Member of the League of American Wheelmen and now I am a Candidate for Director of our new four-hole Golf Club. Also I play Whist on the Train with a Man who once lived in the same House with T. DeWitt Talmage."

Hearing these words the A. D. T. Kid ceased weeping and cheerfully proceeded up an Alley, where he played "Wood Tag."

Moral: *As the Twig is Bent the Tree is Inclined.*

The Fable of the Base Ball Fan who Took the Only Known Cure

Once upon a Time a Base Ball Fan lay on his Death Bed.

He had been a Rooter from the days of Underhand Pitching.

It was simply Pie for him to tell in what year Anse began to play with the Rockfords and what Kelly's Batting Average was the Year he sold for Ten Thousand.

If you asked him who played Center for Boston in 1886 he could tell you quick—right off the Reel. And he was a walking Directory of all the Glass Arms in the Universe.

THE FAN

More than once he had let drive with a Pop Bottle at the Umpire and then Yelled "Robber" until his Pipes gave out. For many Summers he would come Home, one Evening after Another, with his Collar melted, and tell his Wife that the Giants made the Colts look like a lot of Colonial Dames playing Bean Bag in a Weedy Lot back of an Orphan Asylum, and they ought to put a Trained Nurse on Third, and the Dummy at Right needed an Automobile, and the New Man couldn't jump out of a Boat and hit the Water, and the Short-Stop wouldn't be able to pick up a Ball if it was handed to him on a Platter with Water Cress around it, and the Easy One to Third that ought to have been Sponge Cake was fielded like a One-Legged Man with St. Vitus dance trying to do the Nashville Salute.

Of course she never knew what he was Talking about, but she put up with it, Year after Year, mixing Throat Gargle for him and reading the Games to him when he was having his Eyes tested and had to wear a Green Shade.

At last he came to his Ninth Inning and there were Two Strikes called and no Balls, and his Friends knew it was All Day with him. They stood around and tried to forget that he was a Fan. His Wife wept softly and consoled herself with the Thought that possibly he would have amounted to Something if there had been no National Game. She forgave Everything and pleaded for one Final Message. His Lips moved. She leaned over and Listened. He wanted to know if there was Anything in the Morning Papers about the Condition of Bill Lange's Knee.

Moral: *There is a Specific Bacillus for every Classified Disease.*

The Fable of the Unintentional Heroes of Centreville

In Centreville there lived two husky Young Fellows named Bill and Schuyler—commonly abbreviated to Schuy.

They did not find any nourishing Excitement in a Grain Elevator, so they Enlisted to Free Cuba.

The Government gave each of them a Slouch Hat and a prehistoric Firearm. They tied Red Handkerchiefs around their Necks and started for the Front, each with his Head out of the Car Window. They gave the Sioux Yell to everybody along the Track between Centreville and Tampa.

While in Camp they played Double Pedie, smoked Corn-Cob Pipes, and cussed the Rations. They referred to the President of these United States as "Mac," and spoke of the beloved Secretary of War as "Old Alger."

SCHUY

After more or less Delay they went aboard a Boat, and were landed in Cuba, where they began to Shoot at everything that looked Foreign. The hot Rain drenched them, and the tropical Sun steamed them; they had Mud on their clothes, and had to sleep out. When they were unusually Tired and Hungry, they would sing Coon Songs and Roast the War Department.

At last they were ordered Home. On the way back they didn't think of Anything except their two Lady Friends, who worked in the Centreville Steam Laundry.

They rode into Town with a Machete under each Arm, and their Pockets full of Mauser Cartridges.

The first Thing they saw when they alighted from the Train was a Brass Band. It began to play, "See the Conquering Hero Comes."

Then eight Little Girls in White began to strew Flowers in their Pathway.

The Artillery company ripped out a Salute.

Cap Gibbs, who won his Title by owning the first Steam Thrashing Machine ever seen in the County, confronted them with a Red, White, and Blue Sash around him. He Barked in a loud Voice—it was something about Old Glory.

Afterward the Daughters of the Revolution took them in Tow, and escorted them to Pythian Hall, where they were given Fried Chicken, Veal Loaf, Deviled Eggs, Crullers, Preserved Watermelon, Cottage Cheese, Sweet Pickles, Grape Jelly, Soda Biscuit, Stuffed Mangoes, Lemonade, Hickory-Nut Cake, Cookies, Cinnamon Roll, Lemon Pie, Ham, Macaroons, New York Ice Cream, Apple Butter, Charlotte Russe, Peppermint Wafers, and Coffee.

While they were Feeding, the Sons of Veterans Quartet stood on the Rostrum with their Heads together, and sang:

> "Ten-ting to-night! Ten-ting to-night,
> Ten-ting on the old-ah Camp-ground!"

At the first opportunity Bill motioned to Schuyler, and led him into the Anteroom, where they kept the Regalia, the Kindling Wood, and the Mop.

"Say, Schuy, what the Sam Hill does this mean?" he asked; "are we Heroes?"

"That's what Everybody says."

"Do you Believe it?"

"No matter what I believe; I'm goin' to let 'em have their own Way. I may want to Run for Supervisor some Day."

Moral: *If it is your Play to be a Hero, don't Renig.*

The Fable of the Parents who Tinkered with the Offspring

A Married Couple possessed two Boys named Joseph and Clarence. Joseph was much the older. His Parents brought him up on a Plan of their Own. They would not permit him to play with other Boys for fear that he would soil himself, and learn to be Rude and Boisterous.

So they kept Him in the House, and his Mother read to him about Little Rollo, who never lied or cheated, and who grew up to be a Bank President. She seemed to think that a Bank President was above Reproach.

Little Joseph was kept away from the Public Schools, and had to Play Games in the Garret with two Spindly Little Girls. He learned Tatting and the Herring-Bone Stitch. When he was Ten Years of age he could play Chop-Sticks on the Piano; his Ears were Translucent, and his Front Teeth showed like those of a Gray Squirrel.

The other Boys used to make Faces at him over the Back Fence and call him "Sis."

In Due Time he went to College, where he proved to be a Lobster. The Boys held him under the Pump the first Night. When he walked across the Campus, they would

JOSEPH

whistle, "I don't Want to Play in Your Yard." He began to drink Manhattan Cocktails, and he smoked Hemp Cigarettes until he was Dotty. One Day he ran away with a Girl who waited on the Table at his Boarding House, and his Parents Cast him Off. At Present he has charge of the Cloak Room at a Dairy Lunch.

Seeing that the Home Training Experiment had been a Failure in the case of Joseph, the Parents decided to give Clarence a large Measure of Liberty, that he might become Acquainted with the Snares and Temptations of the World while he was Young, and thus be Prepared to side-step the Pitfalls when he was Older. They sent him to the Public

CLARENCE

Schools; they allowed him to roam at large with other Kids, and stay out at Nights; they kept Liquor on the Sideboard.

Clarence stood in with the Toughest Push in Town, and thus became acquainted with the Snares and Temptations of the World. He learned to Chew Tobacco and Spit through his Teeth, shoot Craps and Rush the Can.

When his Father suggested that he enter some Business House, he growled like a Boston Terrier, and told his Father to go Chase Himself.

At present, he is working the Shells with a Circus.

Moral: *It all depends.*

The Fable of How he Never Touched George

A Comic Lover named George was sitting on the Front Porch with a good Side Hold on your old friend Mabel. They were looking into each other's Eyes at Close Range and using a rancid Line of Nursery Talk.

It was the kind of Conversation calculated to Jar a Person.

George murmured that Mabel was George's own Baby-Daby and she Allowed that he was a Tooney-Wooney Ittle Bad Boy to hold his Itsy-Bitsy Bun of a Mabel so tight she could hardly breave. It was a sort of Dialogue that Susan B. Anthony would love to sit up Nights to Read.

MABEL'S FATHER

While they were Clinched, Mabel's Father, a large, Self-Made Man, came down the Stairway and out to the Veranda.

This is where the Fable begins to Differentiate.

Although the Girl's name was Mabel and the Young Man's name was George, and the Father was a Self-Made Man, the Father did *not* Kick the Young Man.

He asked him if he had Anything to Smoke.

George gave him an Imported Panetella and said He didn't believe it was going to Rain. Mabel's Father said it looked Black in the West, but he Reckoned it might blow around, like as not. Mabel said she wouldn't be a bit Surprised if it did blow around.

Mabel's Father told Mabel she could show George where the Ice-Box wuz in case he Expressed a Hankerin', and then he went down street to examine some Fishing Tackle just purchased by a Friend of his in the Hay and Feed Business. Just as Father struck the Cement Walk George changed to the Strangle Hold.

Moral: *The Exception proves the Rule.*

The Fable of the Preacher who Flew his Kite, but Not Because he Wished to Do so

A Certain Preacher became wise to the Fact that he was not making a Hit with his Congregation. The Parishioners did not seem inclined to seek him out after Services and tell him he was a Pansy. He suspected that they were Rapping him on the Quiet.

The Preacher knew there must be something wrong with his Talk. He had been trying to Expound in a clear and straightforward Manner, omitting Foreign Quotations, setting up for illustration of his Points such Historical Characters as were familiar to his Hearers, putting the stubby Old English words ahead of the Latin, and rather flying low along the Intellectual Plane of the Aggregation that chipped in to pay his Salary.

But the Pew-Holders were not tickled. They could Understand everything he said, and they began to think he was Common.

So he studied the Situation and decided that if he wanted to Win them and make everybody believe he was a Nobby and Boss Minister he would have to hand out a little Guff. He fixed it up Good and Plenty.

On the following Sunday Morning he got up in the Lookout and read a Text that didn't mean anything, read from either Direction, and then he sized up his Flock with a

GOOD AND PLENTY

Dreamy Eye and said: "We cannot more adequately voice the Poetry and Mysticism of our Text than in those familiar Lines of the great Icelandic Poet, Ikon Navrojk:

"To hold is not to have—
Under the seared Firmament,
Where Chaos sweeps, and Vast Futurity
Sneers at these puny Aspirations—
There is the full Reprisal."

When the Preacher concluded this Extract from the Well-Known Icelandic Poet he paused and looked downward, breathing heavily through his Nose, like Camille in the Third Act.

GUFF

A Stout Woman in the Front Row put on her Eye-Glasses and leaned forward so as not to miss Anything. A Venerable Harness Dealer over at the Right nodded his Head solemnly. He seemed to recognize the Quotation. Members of the Congregation glanced at one another as if to say: "This is certainly Hot Stuff!"

The Preacher wiped his Brow and said he had no Doubt that every one within the Sound of his Voice remembered what Quarolius had said, following the same Line of Thought. It was Quarolius who disputed the Contention of the great Persian Theologian Ramtazuk, that the Soul in its reaching out after the Unknowable was guided by the Spiritual Genesis of Motive rather than by mere Impulse of Mentality. The Preacher didn't know what all This meant, and he didn't care, but you can rest easy that the Pew-Holders were On in a minute. He talked it off in just the Way that Cyrano talks when he gets Roxane so Dizzy that she nearly falls off the Piazza.

The Parishioners bit their Lower Lips and hungered for more First-Class Language. They had paid their Money for Tall Talk and were prepared to solve any and all Styles of Delivery. They held on to the Cushions and seemed to be having a Nice Time.

The Preacher quoted copiously from the Great Poet Amebius. He recited 18 lines of Greek and then said: "How true this is!" And not a Parishioner batted an Eye.

It was Amebius whose Immortal Lines he recited in order to prove the Extreme Error of the Position assumed in the Controversy by the Famous Italian, Polenta.

He had them Going, and there wasn't a Thing to do. When he would get tired of faking Philosophy he would quote from a Celebrated Poet of Ecuador or Tasmania or some other Seaport Town. Compared with this Verse, all of which was of the same School as the Icelandic Masterpiece, the most obscure and clouded Passage in Robert Browning was like a Plate-Glass Front in a State Street Candy

THE JOYOUS PALM

Store just after the Colored Boy gets through using the Chamois.

After that he became Eloquent, and began to get rid of long Boston Words that hadn't been used before that Season. He grabbed a rhetorical Roman Candle in each Hand and you couldn't see him for the Sparks.

After which he sunk his Voice to a Whisper and talked about the Birds and the Flowers. Then, although there was no Cue for him to Weep, he shed a few real Tears. And there wasn't a dry Glove in the Church.

After he sat down he could tell by the Scared Look of the People in Front that he had made a Ten-Strike.

Did they give him the Joyous Palm that Day? Sure!

VENERABLE HARNESS DEALER

The Stout Lady could not control her Feelings when she told how much the Sermon had helped her. The venerable Harness Dealer said he wished to indorse the Able and Scholarly Criticism of Polenta.

In fact, every one said the Sermon was Superfine and Dandy. The only thing that worried the Congregation was the Fear that if it wished to retain such a Whale it might have to Boost his Salary.

In the Meantime the Preacher waited for some one to come and ask about Polenta, Amebius, Ramtazuk, Quarolius and the great Icelandic Poet, Navrojk. But no one had the Face to step up and confess his Ignorance of these Celebrities. The Pew-Holders didn't even admit among themselves that the Preacher had rung in some New Ones. They stood Pat, and merely said it was an Elegant Sermon.

Perceiving that they would stand for Anything, the Preacher knew what to do after that.

Moral: *Give the People what they Think they want.*

The Fable of Handsome Jethro, who was Simply Cut Out to Be a Merchant

An Illinois Squab came home from Business College with a Zebra Collar and a pair of Tan Shoes big enough for a Coal Miner. When he alighted from the depot one of Ezry

JETHRO

PAW

Folloson's Dray Horses fell over, stricken with the Cramp Colic. The usual Drove of Prominent Citizens who had come down to see that the Train got in and out all right backed away from the Educated Youth and Chewed their Tobacco in Shame and Abashment. They knew that they did not belong on the same Platform with One who had been up yender in Chicago for goin' on Twelve weeks finding out how to be a Business Man. By Heck!

An elderly Man approached the Youth who had lately got next to the Rules of Commerce. The elderly Man was a Yap. He wore a Hickory Shirt, a discouraged Straw Hat, a pair of Barn-Door Pants clinging to one lonely Gallus and woolen

Socks that had settled down over his Plow Shoes. He was shy several Teeth and on his Chin was a Tassel shaped like a Whisk-Broom. If you had thrown a Pebble into this Clump of Whiskers probably you would have scared up a Field Mouse and a couple of Meadow Larks.

"Home agin, Jethro, be ye?" asked the Parent.

"Yeh," replied the Educated Youth. With that he pulled the Corner of a Sassy Silk Handkerchief out of his upper Coat Pocket and ignited a Cigarette that smelt like Burning Leaves in the Fall.

The Business Man went Home, and the Parent followed at a Respectful Distance, now and then remarking to Himself: "Well, I'll just swan to Guinney!"

Brother Lyford came in from the East Eighty to get his Dinner, and there was Jethro in the Hammock reading a Great Work by Archibald Clavering Gunter.

"Git into some Overhauls an' come an' he'p Me this afternoon," said Lyford.

"Oh, rats! Not on your Tintype! I'm too strong to work," replied Jethro, who had learned Oodles of slang up in Chicago, don't you forget it.

So he wouldn't Stand for the Harvest Field that afternoon. In the evening when Paw ast him to Milk he let out an Awful Beller. Next Morning he made a Horrible Beef because he couldn't get Loaf Sugar for his Coffee.

Shortly after Breakfast his Paw lured him into the Barn and Lit on him. He got a good Holt on the Adam's Apple and choked the Offspring until his Tongue stuck out like a Pistil.

"You dosh-burned little Pin-Head o' Misery, you!" exclaimed the Old Man. "Goll bing me if I think you're wuth the Powder to blow you up. You peel them Duds an' git to Work or else mosey right off o' this Farm."

The Son's Feelings were so outraged by this Brutal Treatment that he left the Farm that Day and accepted a position in a Five and Ten-Cent Store, selling Kitchen Utensils that were made of Tin-Foil and Wooden Ware that had been painted in Water Colors. He felt that he was particularly adapted for a Business Career, and, anyway, he didn't propose to go out on No Man's Farm and sweat down his Collar.

After Ten Years of Unremitting Application and Studious Frugality the Business Man had acquired in Real Estate, Personal Property, Stocks, Bonds, Negotiable Paper, and other Collateral, the sum of Nineteen Dollars, but he owed a good deal more than that. Brother Lyford had continued to be a rude and unlettered Country Jake. He had 240 acres of crackin' Corn Land (all tiled), a big red Barn, four Span of good Horses, sixteen Head of Cattle, a likely bunch of Shoats and a Covered Buggy.

Moral: *Drink Deep, or Cut Out the Pierian Spring Altogether.*

The Fable of Paducah's Favorite Comedians and the Mildewed Stunt

Once Upon a Time there was a Specialty Team doing Seventeen Minutes. The Props used in the Act included a Hatchet, a Brick, a Seltzer Bottle, two inflated Bladders and a Slap-Stick. The Name of the Team was Zoroaster and Zendavesta.

These two Troupers began their Professional Career with a Road Circus, working on Canvas in the Morning, and then doing a Refined Knockabout in the Grand Concert or Afterpiece taking place in the Main Arena immediately after the big Show is over.

When each of them could Kick Himself in the Eye and Slattery had pickled his Face so that Stebbins could walk on it, they decided that they were too good to show under a Round Top, so they became Artists. They wanted a Swell Name for the Team, so the Side-Show Announcer, who was something of a Kidder and had attended a Unitarian College, gave them Zoroaster and Zendavesta. They were Stuck on it, and had a Job Printer do some Cards for them.

By utilizing two of Pat Rooney's Songs and stealing a few Gags, they put together Seventeen Minutes and began to play Dates and Combinations.

Zoroaster bought a Cane with a Silver Dog's Head on it, and Zendavesta had a Watch Charm that pulled the Buttonholes out of his Vest.

After every Show, as soon as they Washed Up, they went and stood in front of the Theater, so as to give the Hired Girls a Treat, or else they stood around in the Sawdust and told their Fellow-Workers in the Realm of Dramatic Art

ZOROASTER

how they killed 'em in Decatur and had 'em hollerin' in Lowell, Mass., and got every Hand in the House at St. Paul. Occasionally they would put a Card in the Clipper, saying that they were the Best in the Business, Bar None, and Good Dressers on and off the Stage. Regards to Leonzo Brothers. Charley Diamond please write.

They didn't have to study no New Gags or work up no more Business, becuz they had the Best Act on Earth to begin with. Lillian Russell was jealous of them and they used to know Francis Wilson when he done a Song and Dance.

They had a Scrap Book with a Clipping from a Paducah Paper, which said that they were better than Nat Goodwin. When some Critic who had been bought up by Rival Artists wrote that Zoroaster and Zendavesta ought to be on an Ice Wagon instead of on the Stage, they would get out the Scrap Book and read that Paducah Notice and be thankful that all Critics wasn't Cheap Knockers and that there was one Paper Guy in the United States that reckanized a Neat Turn when he seen it.

But Zoroaster and Zendavesta didn't know that the Dramatic Editor of the Paducah Paper went to a Burgoo Picnic the Day the Actors came to Town, and didn't get back until Midnight, so he wrote his Notice of the Night Owls' performance from a Programme brought to him by the Head Usher at the Opera House, who was also Galley Boy at the Office.

Zoroaster and Zendavesta played the same Sketch for Seventeen Years and made only two important Changes in all that Time. During the Seventh Season Zoroaster changed his Whiskers from Green to Blue. At the beginning of the Fourteenth Year of the Act they bought a new Slap-Stick and put a Card in the Clipper warning the Public to beware of Imitators.

All during the Seventeen Years Zoroaster and Zendavesta continued to walk Chesty and tell People how Good they were. They never could Understand why the Public stood for Mansfield when it could get Zoroaster and Zendavesta. The

ZENDAVESTA

Property Man gave it as his Opinion that Mansfield conned the Critics. Zendavesta said there was only one Critic on the Square, and he was at Paducah.

When the Vodeville Craze came along Zoroaster and Zendavesta took their Paducah Scrap Book over to a Manager, and he Booked them. Zoroaster assured the Manager that Him and his Partner done a Refined Act, suitable for Women and Children, with a strong Finish, which had been the Talk of all Galveston. The Manager put them in between the Trained Ponies and a Legit with a Bad Cold. When a Legit loses his Voice he goes into Vodeville.

Zoroaster and Zendavesta came on very Cocky, and for the 7,800th Time Zoroaster asked Zendavesta:

"Who wuz it I seen you comin' up the Street with?"

Then, for the 7,800th Time, by way of Mirth-Provoking Rejoinder, Zendavesta kicked Zoroaster in the Stomach, after which the Slap-Stick was introduced as a Sub-Motive.

The Manager gave a Sign and the Stage Hands Closed in on the Best Team in the Business, Bar None.

Of course Zoroaster and Zendavesta were very sore at having their Act killed. They said it was no way to treat Artists. The Manager told them they were too Tart for words to tell it and to consider Themselves set back into the Supper Show. Then They saw through the whole Conspiracy. The Manager was Mansfield's Friend and Mansfield was out with his Hammer.

At Present they are doing Two Supper Turns to the Piano Player and a Day Watchman. They are still the Best in the Business, but are being used Dead Wrong. However, they derive some Comfort from reading the Paducah Notice.

Moral: *A Dramatic Editor should never go to a Burgoo Picnic —especially in Kentucky.*

The Fable of Flora and Adolph and a Home Gone Wrong

One morning a Modern Solomon, who had been chosen to preside as Judge in a Divorce Mill, climbed to his Perch and unbuttoned his Vest for the Wearisome Grind. He noticed that the first Case looming up on the Docket was that of Flora Botts vs. Adolph Botts.

The Applicant, Mrs. Botts, and Adolph, the Other Half of the Domestic Sketch, were already inside the Railing, each attempting to look the other out of Countenance.

"Break!" ordered the Judge. "Don't act as if you were at Home. Now, what has Adolph been doing?"

It seemed that she alleged Cruelty, Neglect, Inhuman Treatment, Violent Temper, Threats, etc., etc.

"We have no Chills-and-Fever Music to lend Effect to the

MODERN SOLOMON

Sad Narrative you are about to Spring," said the Judge, looking down at the Plaintiff, who belonged to the Peroxide Tribe. "Furthermore, we will take it for granted that when you first met Defendant your Innocence and Youth made it a Walkaway for his Soft Approaches, and that you had every Reason to believe that he was a Perfect Gentleman. Having disposed of these Preliminaries, let us have the Plot of the Piece."

So she told her Story in a Tremulous, Viola Allen kind of Voice, while her Lawyer wept.

He was ready to Weep for anyone who would hand him $8. Afterthought–make it $7.50.

THE VIPER

It was a Dark Tale of how Botts, the Viperish Defendant, had Sneered at her, called her Oh-Such-Names, humiliated her in the presence of Callers, and nagged her with Sarcastic Comments until her Tender Sensibilities had been worn to a Frazzle.

Then the Defendant went on the Stand and entered a General Denial. He had been all that a Rattling Good Husband could be, but she had been a regular Rudyard Kipling Vampire. She had continued to make his Life one lingering Day-After of Regret. His Record for Patience and Long-Suffering had made Job's Performance look like an Amateur's Half-Try.

"There is more in this Case than appears on the Surface," said the Modern Solomon. "In order to fix the Blame we shall have to dig up the First Cause. I will ask Chemical Flora to tell us the Story of her Past Life."

"My Parents were Poor, but Refined," said Mrs. Botts. "They gave me Every Advantage. After I finished the High School I attended a Conservatory, and every one said I had Talent. I should have been an Elocutionist. Once I went to Rockford and recited "The Tramp's Story," at a Club Social, and I got a Lovely Notice. I am especially good at Dialect Recitations."

"Humorous?" asked the Court.

"Yes, sir; but I can turn right around and be Pathetic all of a sudden if I want to be."

"I suppose that Botts, after he had lived with you for awhile, didn't have any Hankering Desire to hear you Recite," suggested the Modern Solomon.

"That's just it. When I'd offer to get up in Company and speak Something he'd ask me please not to Recite, and if I had to make a Show of myself, for God's Sake not to tackle anything Humorous, with a Conservatory Dialect to it."

"But you wouldn't let him Stop you?"

"Not on your Life."

"I'd believe you, even if you wasn't under Oath. Now, will Mr. Botts answer me one Question? Has he any Ambition on the Side?"

"Although I am a Bookkeeper for a Gravel-Roofing Concern, I have always believed I could Write," replied Adolph Botts. About four years ago I began to prepare the Book for a Comic Opera. A Friend of mine who works in a Hat Store was to Compose the Music. I think he has more Ability than Victor Herbert."

"Did this Friend think Well of your Libretto?" asked the Wise Judge.

"Yes, sir; he said it was the Best Thing that had been done since 'Erminie.' In fact, everybody liked my Book."

"Except your Wife," suggested the Court.

CHEMICAL FLORA

"That's it, exactly. I wanted Sympathy and Encouragement and she gave me the Metallic Laugh. There is one Patter Song in my Opera that Everyone who comes to my House has been Crazy to hear. Whenever I started to Sing it she would talk in a loud Voice. She never seemed to Appreciate my Stuff. I think the Bleach affected her Head."

"Has the Opera been produced?" asked the Court, with Humane Hesitancy.

"No, the Eastern Managers were all tied up with Harry B. Smith," replied Mr. Botts. "Then there's a Prejudice against Western Talent."

"Well, Mr. Botts, in View of all the Evidence, I have

decided to give you a Decree of Divorce from Flo of the Wheaten Tresses," said the Modern Solomon.

"But look here!" exclaimed the Defendant, "I haven't applied for any Divorce."

"You don't have to. I give it to you anyway. As for you, Mrs. Botts, I will give you a Decree also. The Alimony will be $25 per."

"Thanks."

"I don't think you grasp the Decision. When I say that the Alimony is $25 per, I mean that Mrs. Botts will be required to pay that amount to Adolph every week."

"Shameful!"

"Don't be too hasty. I further Decree that Mr. Botts must pay the same Amount to Flora every Week."

"That simply makes it a Stand-Off," remarked Mr. Botts, who was puzzled.

"My idea of the Case, neatly expressed," said the Modern Solomon. "Each of you is Divorced from the Other, and if Either of you ever Marries again, He or She will be jerked before this Tribunal and sentenced to Ten Years of Hard Labor in some Penal Institution."

Whereupon the Court took a Noon Recess of 3½ hours.

Moral: *Genius must ever walk Alone.*

The Fable of the Copper and the Jovial Undergrads

One Night three Well-Bred Young Men, who were entertained at the Best Houses wherever they went, started out to Wreck a College town.

They licked two Hackmen, set fire to an Awning, pulled down many Signs, and sent a Brick through the Front Window of a Tailor Shop. All the Residents of the Town went into the Houses and locked the Doors; Terror brooded over the Community.

A Copper heard the Racket, and saw Women and Children

STUDENT

fleeing to Places of Safety, so he gripped his Club and ran Ponderously, overtaking the three Well-Bred Young Men in a dark part of the Street, where they were Engaged in tearing down a Fence.

He could not see them Distinctly, and he made the Mistake of assuming that they were Drunken Ruffians from the Iron Foundry. So he spoke harshly, and told them to Leave Off breaking the Man's Fence. His Tone and Manner irritated the University Men, who were not accustomed to Rudeness from Menials.

One Student, who wore a Sweater, and whose people butt into the Society Column with Sickening Regularity, started to Tackle Low; he had Bushy Hair and a Thick Neck, and his strong Specialty was to swing on Policemen and Cabbies.

At this, his Companion, whose Great Grandmother had been one of the eight thousand Close Relatives of John Randolph, asked him not to Kill the Policeman. He said the Fellow had made a Mistake, that was all; they were not Muckers; they were Nice Boys, intent on preserving the Traditions of dear old *Alma Mater*.

The Copper could hardly Believe it until they led him to a Street Lamp, and showed him their Engraved Cards and Junior Society Badges; then he Realized that they were All Right. The third Well-Bred Young Man, whose Male Parent got his Coin by wrecking a Building Association in Chicago, then announced that they were Gentlemen, and could Pay for everything they broke. Thus it will be seen that they were Rollicking College Boys and not Common Rowdies.

The Copper, perceiving that he had come very near getting Gay with our First Families, Apologized for Cutting In. The Well-Bred Young Men forgave him, and then took his Club away from him, just to Demonstrate that there were no Hard Feelings. On the way back to the Seat of Learning they captured a Night Watchman, and put him down a Man-Hole.

Moral: *Always select the Right Sort of Parents before you start in to be Rough.*

The Fable of a Statesman who Couldn't Make Good

Once there was a Bluff whose Long Suit was Glittering Generalities.

He hated to Work and it hurt his Eyes to read Law, but on a Clear Day he could be heard a Mile, so he became a Statesman.

Whenever the Foresters had a Picnic they invited him to make the Principal Address, because he was the only Orator who could beat out the Merry-Go-Round.

STATESMAN

The Habit of Dignity enveloped him.

Upon his Brow Deliberation sat. He wore a Fireman's moustache and a White Lawn Tie, and he loved to Talk about the Flag.

At a Clam-Bake in 1884 he hurled Defiance at all the Princes and Potentates of Europe, and the Sovereign Voters, caught up by his Matchless Eloquence and Unswerving Courage, elected him to the Legislature.

While he was in the Legislature he discovered that these United States were an Asylum for the Down-Trodden and oppressed of the Whole World, and frequently called Attention to the Fact. When some one asked him if he was cutting up any Easy Money or would it be safe for a Man with a Watch to go to Sleep in the Same Room with him, he would take a Drink of Water and begin to plead for Cuba.

Once an Investigating Committee got after him and he was about to be Shown Up for Dallying with Corporations, but he put on a fresh White Tie and made a Speech about our Heroic Dead on a Hundred Battle-Fields, and Most People said it was simply Impossible for such a Thunderous Patriot to be a Crook. So he played the Glittering Generality stronger than ever.

In Due Time he Married a Widow of the Bantam Division. The Reason she married him was that he looked to her to be

THE BANTAM

a Coming Congressman and she wanted to get a Whack at Washington Society. Besides, she lived in a Flat and the Janitor would not permit her to keep a Dog.

About Ten Days after they were Married he came Home at 4 A.M. in a Sea-Going Hack and he was Saturated. Next Morning she had him up on the Carpet and wanted to know How About It.

He arose and put his Right Hand inside of his Prince Albert Coat and began.

"Madam," he said, "During a Long, and, I trust, a not altogether fruitless Career as a Servant of the Peepul, I have always stood in the Fierce Light of Publicity, and my Record is an Open Book which he who runs may——"

"Nix! Nix!" she said, rapping for order with a Tea-Cup. "Let go of the Flying Rings. Get back to the Green Earth!"

He dilated his Nostrils and said: "From the Rock-Bound Hills of Maine in the North to the Everglades of Florida——"

"Forget the Everglades," she said, rapping again. "That Superheated Atmosphere may have a certain Tonic Effect on the Hydrocephalous Voter, but if you want to adjust yourself with Wifey, you come down to Cases."

So he went out after Breakfast and bought a $22 Hat in order to Square himself.

Moral: *Some Women should be given the Right to Vote.*

The Fable of the Coming Champion who was Delayed

In a certain Athletic Club which rented two rooms over a Tin-Shop there was one Boy who could put it All Over the other Members.

He knew how to Jab and Counter and Upper-Cut and Bore in with the Left and Play for the Wind. He had Lumps on his Arms and a good Pair of Shoulders, and every one in the Club told him he had the makings of a World-Beater. He used to coax Grocery Clerks and Grammar-School Children to put on the Gloves with him, and then he would go around them, like a Cooper around a Barrel, and Trim them right and proper.

His friends would stand and watch him make Monkeys of these anemic Amateurs, and gradually the Conviction grew within them that he could Lick anybody of his Weight. The Boy believed them when they told him he ought to go after the Top-Notchers.

He gave up his Job in the Planing Mill and became a Pugilist. The Proprietor of a Cigar Store acted as his Manager, and began to pay his Board. This Manager was

MANAGER

Foxy. He told the Boy that before Tackling the Championship Class it would be better to go out and beat a lot of Fourth-Raters, thereby building a Reputation and at the same time getting here and there a Mess of the Long Green.

In the same Town there was an Undertaker who had Sporting Blood in his Veins, and he sought out the Manager and made a Match in behalf of an Unknown.

The boy went into Training in a Stable. He had a yellow Punching Bag, a Sponge, a Bath-Robe and several Towels. Two Paper-Hangers who were out of Work acted as his Trainers. They rubbed him with Witch Hazel all day, and in the Evening the Boy stood around in a Sweater and Talked out of the corner of his Mouth. He said he was Trained to the Minute, as Hard as Nails and Fit as a Fiddle, and he would make Mr. Unknown jump out of the Ring.

As the Day of the Battle approached it came out that the Unknown was a Scrapper who had been fairly Successful at one Time, but had ceased to be a Live One several Years before. He was imported especially for this Contest with the Coming Champion.

When he arrived in Town it was evident that he lacked Condition. He had been dieting himself on Pie and Beer, and any Expert, such as the Cigar Store Man, could tell by looking at him that his Abdomen was not hard enough to withstand those crushing Body Blows such as the Boy was in the Habit of Landing—on the Punching Bag. Accordingly the Word went around that the imported Pug was too Fat and had bad Wind.

It began to resemble a Cinch.

The Manager went out and bet more Money, and the Coming Champion was Nervous for fear that he would kill the Has-Been if he connected too strong on the Point of the Jaw. He thought it would be better to wear him down with Short-Arm blows and make him Quit. He had read that it was Dangerous to punish a Physical Wreck, who might have Heart Trouble or something like that. The Boy was a Professional Pugilist, but he had Humane Instincts.

THE COMING CHAMPION

When the Boy came to the Train which was to carry the Participants and the Spectators to the Battle-Field he was attended by four Comrades, who had Ice, Beef Tea, Brandy, Alcohol, Blankets and other Paraphernalia. They made a Couch for him in the Baggage Car, and had him lie down, so that he might conserve all his Strength and step into the Ring as fresh as possible. The so-called Unknown had no one to Handle him. He sat Alone in the Men's Car, with a queer Telescope Valise on his Knees, and he smoked a Cigarette, which was in direct Violation of all the Rules of Training.

At last the Company arrived at the Secluded Spot, and a Ring was staked out.

The Coming Champion was received with Loud Cheers. He wore a new Pair of Gymnasium Shoes, spotless Trunks, and around his Waist was an American Flag, presented by his Admirers in the Athletic Club.

In a few Moments the Imported Scrapper came into the Ring, attended by the Sporty Undertaker. He wore an old Pair of Bike Shoes and faded Work Trousers, chopped off at the Knees, while his Belt was a Shawl-Strap. He was chewing Gum.

After he put on the Gloves he looked over at the Coming Champion and remarked to the Undertaker that he (the Coming Champion) seemed to be a Nice Young Fellow. After which he Yawned slightly, and wanted to know what Time they would get a Train back to Town.

The Bell rang, and there in the Center of the Ring stood the Tottering Has-Been and the Coming Champion.

The Has-Been was crouched, with his Head drawn in, turtle-fashion, his Legs spraddled, and oh, the hard, vicious Expression on that Face, as he Fiddled Short and looked intently at the Coming Champion's Feet. This was a very confusing and unprofessional Thing to do, as the Boy had not been accustomed to boxing with People who looked at his Feet. He wondered if there was anything the matter with his Gymnasium Shoes.

In a Moment or two he saw that the Physical Wreck was afraid to Lead, so he did some nimble Foot Work, and his Gloves began to describe Parabolas—then all at once somebody turned off the Sunshine.

They threw Cold Water on him, held a Bottle of Ammonia to his Nose and stuck Pins in under his Finger-Nails.

At last his Eye-Lids fluttered, and he turned a dim and filmy Gaze on his faithful Seconds gathered about him.

"Oh, how the Birds sing!" he murmured. "And see! The Aurora Borealis is trying to climb over Pain's Fire-Works."

"Cheer up!" said the Manager. "He took a Mean Advan-

AND SEE!

tage of you and Hit you when you wasn't Looking."

"Ah, yes, it all comes back to me. Did I win?"

"Not quite," replied the Manager, who feared to tell him the whole Truth.

"You say he Hit me?" asked the Coming Champion.

"Yes."

"With a Casting?"

"We couldn't tell. He was in such a Hurry."

All this Time the Victor was sitting on the Station Platform with the Undertaker. He was Remarking that it seemed to be a very Purty Country thereabouts, and he'd often wished he could close in on enough of the Gilt to buy him a nice piece of Land somewhere, inasmuch as he regarded a Farmer as the most independent Man on Earth.

Next week there was a familiar Name back on the Time-Card at the Planing Mill.

Moral: *In all the Learned Professions, Many are Called but Few are Chosen.*

The Fable of the Lawyer who Brought In a Minority Report

At a Bazaar, the purpose of which was to Hold Up the Public for the Benefit of a Worthy Cause, there were many Schemes to induce Visitors to let go of their Assets. One of the most likely Grafts perpetrated by the astute Management was a Voting Contest to Determine who was the Most Beautiful and Popular Young Lady in the City. It cost Ten Cents to cast one Vote. The Winner of the Contest was to receive a beautiful Vase, with Roses on it.

A prominent Young Lawyer, who was Eloquent, Good Looking, and a Leader in Society, had been selected to make the Presentation Speech after the Votes had been counted.

In a little while the Contest had narrowed down until it was Evident that either the Brewer's Daughter or the Contractor's Daughter was the Most Beautiful and Popular Young Lady in the City. The Brewer and his Friends pushed Ten Dollar Bills into the Ballot Box, while the Contractor, just before the Polls closed, slipped in a Check for One Hundred Dollars.

When the Votes were counted, the Management of the Bazaar was pleased to learn that the Sixty-Cent Vase had Netted over Seven Hundred Dollars. It was Announced that the Contractor's Daughter was exactly Nine Dollars and Twenty Cents more Beautiful and Popular than the Brewer's Daughter.

Thereupon the Committee requested that the Eloquent

Young Lawyer step to the Rostrum and make the Presentation Speech. There was no Response; the Young Lawyer had Disappeared.

One of the Members of the Committee started on a Search for him, and found him in a dusky Corner of the Japanese Tea Garden, under the Paper Lanterns, making a Proposal of Marriage to a Poor Girl who had not received one Vote

Moral: *Never believe a Relative.*

The Fable of the Two Mandolin Players and the Willing Performer

A Very Attractive Debutante knew two Young Men who called on her every Thursday Evening, and brought their Mandolins along.

They were Conventional Young Men, of the Kind that you see wearing Spring Overcoats in the Clothing Advertisements. One was named Fred, and the other was Eustace.

The Mothers of the Neighborhood often remarked, "What Perfect Manners Fred and Eustace have!" Merely as an aside it may be added that Fred and Eustace were more Popular with the Mothers than they were with the Younger Set, although no one could say a Word against either of them. Only it was rumored in Keen Society that they didn't Belong. The Fact that they went Calling in a Crowd, and took their Mandolins along, may give the Acute Reader some Idea of the Life that Fred and Eustace held out to the Young Women of their Acquaintance.

The Debutante's name was Myrtle. Her Parents were very Watchful, and did not encourage her to receive Callers, except such as were known to be Exemplary Young Men. Fred and Eustace were a few of those who escaped the Black List. Myrtle always appeared to be glad to see them, and they regarded her as a Darned Swell Girl.

Fred's Cousin came from St. Paul on a Visit; and one

FRED AND EUSTACE

Day, in the Street, he saw Myrtle, and noticed that Fred tipped his Hat, and gave her a Stage Smile.

"Oh, Queen of Sheba!" exclaimed the Cousin from St. Paul, whose name was Gus, as he stood stock still, and watched Myrtle's Reversible Plaid disappear around a Corner. "She's a Bird. Do you know her well?"

"I know her Quite Well," replied Fred, coldly. "She is a Charming Girl."

"She is all of that. You're a great Describer. And now what Night are you going to take me around to Call on her?"

Fred very naturally Hemmed and Hawed. It must be remembered that Myrtle was a member of an Excellent Family, and had been schooled in the Proprieties, and it was not to be supposed that she would crave the Society of slangy old Gus, who had an abounding Nerve, and furthermore was as Fresh as the Mountain Air.

He was the Kind of Fellow who would see a Girl twice, and then, upon meeting her the Third Time, he would go up and straighten her Cravat for her, and call her by her First Name.

Put him into a Strange Company—en route to a Picnic—and by the time the Baskets were unpacked he would have a Blonde all to himself, and she would have traded her Fan for his College Pin.

If a Fair-Looker on the Street happened to glance at him Hard he would run up and seize her by the Hand, and convince her that they had Met. And he always Got Away with it, too.

In a Department Store, while waiting for the Cash Boy to come back with the Change, he would find out the Girl's Name, her Favorite Flower, and where a Letter would reach her.

Upon entering a Parlor Car at St. Paul he would select a Chair next to the Most Promising One in Sight, and ask her if she cared to have the Shade lowered.

Before the Train cleared the Yards he would have the Porter bringing a Foot-Stool for the Lady.

At Hastings he would be asking her if she wanted Something to Read.

At Red Wing he would be telling her that she resembled Maxine Elliott, and showing her his Watch, left to him by his Grandfather, a Prominent Virginian.

At La Crosse he would be reading the Menu Card to her, and telling her how different it is when you have Some One to join you in a Bite.

At Milwaukee he would go out and buy a Bouquet for her, and when they rode into Chicago they would be looking out of the same Window, and he would be arranging for their Baggage with the Transfer Man. After that they would be Old Friends.

Now, Fred and Eustace had been at School with Gus, and they had seen his Work, and they were not disposed to Introduce him into One of the most Exclusive Homes in the City.

They had known Myrtle for many Years; but they did not dare to Address her by her First Name, and they were Positive that if Gus attempted any of his usual Tactics with her she would be Offended; and, naturally enough, they would be Blamed for bringing him to the House.

But Gus insisted. He said he had seen Myrtle, and she Suited him from the Ground up, and he proposed to have Friendly Doings with her. At last they told him they would take him if he promised to Behave. Fred Warned him that Myrtle would frown down any Attempt to be Familiar on Short Acquaintance, and Eustace said that as long as he had known Myrtle he had never Presumed to be Free and Forward with her. He had simply played the Mandolin. That was as Far Along as he had ever got.

Gus told them not to Worry about him. All he asked was a Start. He said he was a Willing Performer, but as yet he never had been Disqualified for Crowding. Fred and Eustace took this to mean that he would not Overplay his Attentions, so they escorted him to the House.

As soon as he had been Presented, Gus showed her where to sit on the Sofa, then he placed himself about Six Inches away and began to Buzz, looking her straight in the Eye. He said that when he first saw her he Mistook her for Miss Prentice, who was said to be the Most Beautiful Girl in St. Paul, only, when he came closer, he saw that it couldn't be Miss Prentice, because Miss Prentice didn't have such Lovely Hair. Then he asked her the Month of her Birth and told her Fortune, thereby coming nearer to Holding her Hand within Eight Minutes than Eustace had come in a Lifetime.

"Play something, Boys," he Ordered, just as if he had paid them Money to come along and make Music for him.

They unlimbered their Mandolins and began to play a Sousa March. He asked Myrtle if she had seen the New

Moon. She replied that she had not, so they went Outside.

When Fred and Eustace finished the first Piece, Gus appeared at the open Window, and asked them to play "The Georgia Camp-Meeting," which had always been one of his Favorites.

So they played that, and when they had Concluded there came a Voice from the Outer Darkness, and it was the Voice of Myrtle. She said: "I'll tell you what to Play; play the Intermezzo."

Fred and Eustace exchanged Glances. They began to Perceive that they had been backed into a Siding. With a few Potted Palms in front of them, and two Cards from the Union, they would have been just the same as a Hired Orchestra.

But they played the Intermezzo and felt Peevish. Then they went to the Window and looked out. Gus and Myrtle were sitting in the Hammock, which had quite a Pitch toward the Center. Gus had braced himself by Holding to the back of the Hammock. He did not have his Arm around Myrtle, but he had it Extended in a Line parallel with her Back. What he had done wouldn't Justify a Girl in saying, "Sir!" but it started a Real Scandal with Fred and Eustace. They saw that the only Way to Get Even with her was to go Home without saying "Good Night." So they slipped out the Side Door, shivering with Indignation.

After that, for several Weeks, Gus kept Myrtle so Busy that she had no Time to think of considering other Candidates. He sent Books to her Mother, and allowed the Old Gentleman to take Chips away from him at Poker.

They were Married in the Autumn, and Father-in-Law took Gus into the Firm, saying that he had needed a good Pusher for a Long Time.

At the Wedding the two Mandolin Players were permitted to act as Ushers.

Moral: *To get a fair Trial of Speed, use a Pace-Maker.*

The Fable of the Man who Didn't Care for Story-Books

Once there was a blue Dyspeptic, who attempted to Kill Time by reading Novels, until he discovered that all Books of Fiction were a Mockery.

After a prolonged Experience he came to know that every Specimen of Light Reading belonged to one of the following Divisions:

1. The Book that Promises well until you reach the Plot, and then you Remember that you read it Summer before last.

2. The book with the Author's Picture as a Frontispiece. The Author is very Cocky. He has his Overcoat thrown back, so as to reveal the Silk Lining. That Settles it!

3. The Book that runs into a Snarl of Dialect on the third Page and never gets out.

4. The delectable Yarn about a Door-Mat Thief, who truly loves the Opium Fiend. Jolly Story of the Slums.

5. The Book that begins with a twenty-page Description of Sloppy Weather: "Long swirls of riven Rain beat somberly upon the misty Panes," etc. etc.

You turn to the last Chapter to see if it Rains all the way through the Book. This last Chapter is a Give-Away. It condenses the whole Plot and dishes up the Conclusion. After that, who would have the Nerve to wade through the Two Hundred and Forty intermediate Pages?

6. The Book in which the Pictures tell the Story. After you have seen the Pictures there is no need to wrestle with the Text.

7. The Book that begins with a Murder Mystery—charming Picture of Gray-Haired Man discovered Dead in his Library—Blood splashed all over the Furniture—Knife of Curious Design lying on Floor.

You know at once that the most Respected and least *sus*pected Personage in the Book committed the awful Crime, but you haven't the Heart to Track him down and compel him to commit Suicide.

8. The Book that gets away with one Man asking another: "By Jove, who is that Dazzling Beauty in the Box?"

The Man who asks this Question has a Name which sounds like the Title of a Sleeping Car.

You feel instinctively that he is going to be all Mixed Up with that Girl in the Box before Chapter XII. is reached; but who can take any real Interest in the Love Affairs of a Man with such a Name?

9. The Book that tells all about Society and how Tough it is. Even the Women drink Brandy and Soda, smoke Cigarettes, and Gamble. The clever Man of the World, who says all the Killing Things, is almost as Funny as Ally Sloper. An irritable Person, after reading nine Chapters of this kind of High Life, would be ready to go Home and throw his Grandmother into the Fire.

10. The dull, gray Book, or the Simple Annals of John Gardensass. A Careful Study of American Life.

In Chapter I. he walks along the Lane, stepping first on one Foot and then on the Other, enters a House by the Door, and sits in a four-legged wooden Chair, looking out through a Window with Glass in it. Book denotes careful Observation. Nothing happens until Page 150. Then John decides to sell the Cow. In the Final Chapter he sits on a Fence and Whittles. True Story, but What's the Use?

Why continue? The Dyspeptic said that when he wanted something really Fresh and Original in the Line of Fiction he read the Prospectus of a Mining Corporation.

Moral: *Only the more Rugged Mortals should attempt to Keep Up on Current Literature.*

The Fable of the Brash Drummer and the Peach who Learned that There Were Others

A Well-Fixed Mortgage Shark, residing at a Way Station, had a Daughter whose Experience was not as large as her prospective Bank Roll. She had all the component Parts of a Peach, but she didn't know how to make a Showing, and there was nobody in Town qualified to give her a quiet Hunch.

She got her Fashion Hints from a Trade Catalogue, and took her Tips on Etiquette and Behavior from the Questions and Answers Department of an Agricultural Monthly.

The Girl and her Father lived in a big White House, with Evergreen Trees and whitewashed Dornicks in front of it, and a Wind-Pump at the rear. Father was a good deal the same kind of a Man as David Harum, except that he didn't let go of any Christmas Presents, or work the Soft Pedal when he had a chance to apply a Crimp to some Widow who had seen Better Days. In fact, Daughter was the only one on Earth who could induce him to Loosen Up.

Now, it happened that there came to this Town every Thirty Days a brash Drummer, who represented a Tobacco House. He was a Gabby Young Man, and he could Articulate at all Times, whether he had anything to Say or not.

One night, at a Lawn Fête given by the Ladies of the Methodist Congregation, he met Daughter. She noticed that his Trousers did not bag at the Knees; also that he wore a superb Ring. They strolled under the Maples, and he talked what is technically known as Hot Air. He made an Impression considerably deeper than himself. She promised to Correspond.

On the occasion of his next Visit to the Way Station, he let her wear his Ring, and made a Wish, while she took him riding in the Phaeton. He began to carry her Photograph in his Watch, and show it to the Boys employed at the House. Sometimes he would fold over one of her Letters so they could see how it started out. He said the Old Man had

Nothing But, and he proposed to make it a case of Marry. Truly, it seemed that he was the principal Cake in the Pantry, and little did he suspect that he could be Frosted.

But Daughter, after much Pleading, induced Father to send her to a Finishing School in the East. (A Finishing School is a Place at which Young Ladies are taught how to give the Quick Finish to all Persons who won't do.)

At School, the Daughter tied up with a Chum, who seldom overlooked a Wednesday Matinee, and she learned more in three Weeks than her Childhood Home could have shown her in three Centuries.

Now she began to see the other Kind; the Kind that Wears a Cutaway, with a White Flower, in the Morning, a Frock, with Violets, in the Afternoon, and a jimmy little Tuxedo at Night.

For the first time she began to listen to Harness that had Chains to it, and she rode in Vehicles that permitted her to glance in at the Second Stories.

She stopped wearing Hats, and began to choose Confections. She selected them Languidly, three at a time.

Then the Bill to the Way Station, and Father down with Heart Failure.

She kept Mr. Sothern's Picture on her Dresser, with two Red Candles burning in front of it, and every time she thought of Gabby Will, the Crackerjack Salesman, she reached for the Peau d'Espagne and sprayed herself.

* * * * * * *

One Day when the Tobacco Salesman came up Main Street with his Grips, on his way to visit the Trade, he met the Drug Clerk, who told him that She was Home on a Visit. So he hurried through with his Work, got a Shave, changed ends on his Cuffs, pared his Nails, bought a box of Marshmallows, and went out to the House.

Daughter was on the Lawn, seated under a Canopy that had set Father back thirty-two Dollars. There was a Hired Hand sprinkling the Grass with a Hose, and as Will, the

Conversational Drummer, came up the Long Walk, Daughter called to the Hired Hand, and said: "Johnson, there is a Strange Man coming up the Walk; change the Direction of the Stream somewhat, else you may Dampen him."

The Drummer approached her, feeling of his Necktie, and wondered if she would up and Kiss him, right in broad Daylight. She didn't. Daughter allowed a rose-colored Booklet, by Guy de Maupassant, to sink among the Folds of her French Gown, and then she Looked at him, and said: "All Goods must be delivered at the Rear."

"Don't you Know me?" he asked.

"Rully, it seems to me I have seen you, Somewhere," she replied, "but I cahn't place you. Are you the Man who tunes the Piano?"

"Don't you remember the night I met you at the Lawn Fête?" he asked; and then, Chump that he was, and all Rattled, he told her his Name, instead of giving her the scorching Come-Back that he composed next Day, when it was Too Late.

"I meet so many People traveling about," she said; "I cahn't remember all of them, you know. I dare say you called to see Pu-pah; he will be here Presently."

Then she gave him "Some one's else," "Neyether," "Savoir-Faire," and a few other Crisp Ones, hot from the Finishing School, after which she asked him how the Dear Villagers were coming on. He reminded her that he did not live in the Town. She said: "Only Fahncy!" and he said he guessed he'd have to be Going, as he had promised a Man to meet him at Jordan's Store before the Bank closed.

As he moved toward the St. Nicholas Hotel he kept his Hand on his Solar Plexus. At five o'clock he rode out of Town on a Local.

Moral: *Anybody can Win unless there happens to be a Second Entry.*

The Fable of Sister Mae, who Did as Well as Could Be Expected

Two Sisters lived in Chicago, the Home of Opportunity.

Luella was a Good Girl, who had taken Prizes at the Mission Sunday School, but she was Plain, much. Her Features did not seem to know the value of Team Work. Her Clothes fit her Intermittently, as it were. She was what could be called a Lumpy Dresser. But she had a good Heart.

Luella found Employment at a Hat Factory. All she had to do was to put Red Linings in Hats for the Country Trade; and every Saturday Evening, when Work was called on account of Darkness, the Boss met her as she went out and crowded three Dollars on her.

The other Sister was Different.

She began as Mary, then changed to Marie, and her Finish was Mae.

From earliest Youth she had lacked Industry and Application.

She was short on Intellect but long on Shape.

The Vain Pleasures of the World attracted her. By skipping the Long Words she could read how Rupert Banisford led Sibyl Gray into the Conservatory and made Love that scorched the Begonias. Sometimes she just Ached to light out with an Opera Company.

When she couldn't stand up Luella for any more Car Fare she went out looking for Work, and hoping she wouldn't find it. The sagacious Proprietor of a Lunch Room employed her as Cashier. In a little While she learned to count Money, and could hold down the Job.

Marie was a Strong Card. The Male Patrons of the Establishment hovered around the Desk long after paying their Checks. Within a Month the Receipts of the Place had doubled.

It was often remarked that Marie was a Pippin. Her Date Book had to be kept on the Double Entry System.

Although her Grammar was Sad, it made no Odds. Her Picture was on many a Button.

A Credit Man from the Wholesale House across the Street told her that any time she wanted to see the Telegraph Poles rush past, she could tear Transportation out of his Book. But Marie turned him down for a Bucket Shop Man, who was not Handsome, but was awful Generous.

They were Married, and went to live in a Flat with a Quarter-Sawed Oak Chiffonier and Pink Rugs. She was Mae at this Stage of the Game.

Shortly after this, Wheat jumped twenty-two points, and the Husband didn't do a Thing.

Mae bought a Thumb Ring and a Pug Dog, and began to speak of the Swede Help as "The Maid."

Then she decided that she wanted to live in a House, because, in a Flat, One could never be sure of One's Neighbors. So they moved into a Sarcophagus on the Boulevard, right in between two Old Families, who had made their Money soon after the Fire, and Ice began to form on the hottest Days.

Mae bought an Automobile, and blew her Allowance against Beauty Doctors. The Smell of Cooking made her Faint, and she couldn't see where the Working Classes came in at all.

When she attended the theater a Box was none too good. Husband went along, in evening clothes and a Yachting Cap, and he had two large Diamonds in his Shirt Front.

Sometimes she went to a Vogner Concert, and sat through it, and she wouldn't Admit any more that the Russell Brothers, as the Irish Chambermaids, hit her just about Right.

She was determined to break into Society if she had to use an Ax.

At last she Got There; but it cost her many a Reed Bird and several Gross of Cold Quarts.

In the Hey-Day of Prosperity did Mae forget Luella? No, indeed.

She took Luella away from the Hat Factory, where the Pay was three Dollars a Week, and gave her a Position as Assistant Cook at five Dollars.

Moral: *Industry and Perseverance bring a sure Reward.*

The Fable of How the Fool-Killer Backed Out of a Contract

The Fool-Killer came along the Pike Road one Day and stopped to look at a Strange Sight.

Inside of a Barricade were several Thousands of Men, Women and Children. They were moving restlessly among the trampled Weeds, which were clotted with Watermelon Rinds, Chicken Bones, Straw and torn Paper Bags.

It was a very hot Day. The People could not sit down. They shuffled Wearily and were pop-eyed with Lassitude and Discouragement.

A stifling Dust enveloped them. They Gasped and Sniffled. Some tried to alleviate their Sufferings by gulping down a Pink Beverage made of Drug-Store Acid, which fed the Fires of Thirst.

Thus they wove and interwove in the smoky Oven. The Whimper or the faltering Wail of Children, the quavering Sigh of overlaced Women, and the long-drawn Profanity of Men—these were what the Fool-Killer heard as he looked upon the Suffering Throng.

"Is this a new Wrinkle on Dante's Inferno?" he asked of the Man on the Gate, who wore a green Badge marked "Marshal," and was taking Tickets.

"No, sir; this is a County Fair," was the reply.

"Why do the People congregate in the Weeds and allow the Sun to warp them?"

"Because Everybody does it."

"Do they Pay to get in?"

"You know it."

"Can they Escape?"

"They can, but they prefer to Stick."

The Fool-Killer hefted his Club and then looked at the Crowd and shook his Head doubtfully.

"I can't tackle that Outfit to-day," he said. "It's too big a Job."

So he went on into Town, and singled out a Main Street Merchant who refused to Advertise.

Moral: *People who expect to be Luny will find it safer to travel in a Bunch.*

The Fable of the Caddy who Hurt His Head While Thinking

One Day a Caddy sat in the Long Grass near the Ninth Hole and wondered if he had a Soul. His Number was 27, and he almost had forgotten his Real Name.

As he sat and Meditated, two Players passed him. They were going the Long Round, and the Frenzy was upon them.

They followed the Gutta Percha Balls with the intent swiftness of trained Bird Dogs, and each talked feverishly of Brassy Lies, and getting past the Bunker, and Lofting to the Green, and Slicing into the Bramble—each telling his own Game to the Ambient Air, and ignoring what the other Fellow had to say.

As they did the St. Andrews Full Swing for eighty Yards apiece and then Followed Through with the usual Explanations of how it Happened, the Caddy looked at them and Reflected that they were much inferior to his Father.

His Father was too Serious a Man to get out in Mardi Gras Clothes and hammer a Ball from one Red Flag to another.

His Father worked in a Lumber Yard.

He was an Earnest Citizen, who seldom Smiled, and he

MEDITATIVE CADDY

knew all about the Silver Question and how J. Pierpont Morgan done up a Free People on the Bond Issue.

The Caddy wondered why it was that his Father, a really Great Man, had to shove Lumber all day and could seldom get one Dollar to rub against another, while these superficial Johnnies who played Golf all the Time had Money to Throw at the Birds. The more he Thought the more his Head ached.

Moral: *Don't try to Account for Anything.*

The Fable of the Martyr who Liked the Job

Once in a Country Town there was a Man with a Weak Back.

He could put a Grindstone into a Farm Wagon if any one wanted to bet him the Segars, but every time he lifted an Ax, something caught him right in the Spine and he had to go into the House and lie down. So his Wife took Boarders and did the Cooking herself.

He was willing to divide the Labor, however; so he did the Marketing. Only, when he had bought the Victuals, he would squat on a Shoe-Box with the Basket between his Legs and say that he couldn't see what Congress wuz thinkin' of.

He had certain Theories in regard to the Alaskan Boundary and he was against any Anglo-American Alliance becuz Uncle Sam could take care of himself at any Turn in the Road, comin' right down to it, and the American People wuz superior to any other Naytionality in every Way, Shape, Manner and Form, as fur as that's concerned. Then his Wife would have to send Word for him to come on with the Groceries so she could get Dinner.

Nearly Everybody Sympathized with her, because she had to put up with such a big Hulk of a no-account Husband. She was looked upon as a Martyr.

One Day the Husband was Sunstruck, being too Lazy to move into the Shade, and next Day he Passed Away without an Effort. The Widow gave him the best Funeral of the Year, and then put all the Money she could rake and scrape into a Marble Shaft marked "At Rest."

A good many People said she was Better Off without him, and it was certainly a Good Riddance of Bad Rubbish.

They hoped that if she ever Married again she'd pick out Somebody that wuzn't afraid to Work, and had Gumption enough to pound Sand into a Rat-Hole.

There was General Satisfaction when she became the Wife of Mr. Gladden, who owned the General Store. He built a new House, hired a Girl and had the Washing sent out. She could go into the Store and pick out Anything she wanted, and he took her riding in his new Runabout every Evening.

Consequently, she was very Miserable, thinking of the Jewel she had lost.

Moral: *If the Woman thinks he's All Right, you keep on your own Side of the Fence.*

The Fable of the Bohemian who Had Hard Luck

Once upon a Time there was a Brilliant but Unappreciated Chap who was such a Thorough Bohemian that Strangers usually mistook him for a Tramp.

Would he brush his Clothes? Not he. When he wore a Collar he was Ashamed of himself. He had Pipe-Ashes on his Coat and Vest. He seldom Combed his Hair, and Never Shaved.

Every Evening he ate an Imitation Dinner, at a forty-cent Table d'Hôte, with a Bottle of Writing Fluid thrown in. He had formed a little Salon of Geniuses, who also were out of Work, and they loved to Loll around on their Shoulder-Blades and Laugh Bitterly at the World.

The main Bohemian was an Author. After being Turned Down by numerous Publishers, he had decided to write for Posterity. Posterity hadn't heard anything about it, and couldn't get out an Injunction.

He knew his Works were good, because all the Free and Untrammeled Souls in the Spaghetti Joint told him so. He would read them a Little Thing of his Own about Wandering in the Fields with Lesbia, and then he would turn to a Friend, whose Face was all covered with Human Ivy, and ask him, point blank: "Is it, or is it not, Better than the Dooley Stuff?"

"There is no Comparison," would be the Reply, coming through the Foliage.

Wandering in the Fields with Lesbia! Lesbia would have done Well. If he had Wandered in the Fields at any Time he would have been Pinched on Suspicion that he was out for Turnips.

The sure-enough Bohemian was a Scathing Critic. If Brander Matthews only knew some of the Things said about him, there would be Tear Marks on his Pillow. And Howells, too. Bah! My, but he was Caustic.

The way he burned up Magazine Writers, it's a Wonder they didn't get after him for Arson.

One day, while standing on the Front Stoop at his Boarding House, trying to think of some one who would submit to a Touch, a Flower Pot fell from a Window Ledge above him, and hit him on the Head. He was put into an Ambulance and taken to a Hospital, where the Surgeons clipped his Hair short, in order to take Three Stitches. While he was still Unconscious, and therefore unable to Resist, they Scrubbed him with Castile Soap, gave him a good Shave, and put him into a snowy-white Gown.

His Friends heard of the Accident, and went to the Hospital to offer Condolence. When they found him he was so Clean and Commonplace that they lost all Respect for him.

Moral: *Get a good Make-Up and the Part plays itself.*

The Fable of The Brotherhood of States & The Wife Who Was Responsible for the Jubilee

Hubby had promised to be home early for Dinner. He had one Foot on the Step of the Street-Car when he happened to remember that his Wife had told him to bring home a Basket of Gem Melons, because the Grocer did not keep the Kind she liked.

Hubby objected to playing Pack-Pony on the Streets, but he knew there would be a catch-as-catch-can Talking Match if he failed to show up with those Melons, so he turned reluctantly and allowed the Car to go its Way.

He sought a Delicatessen Store and bought a 5-pound Basket of undersized Canteloupes that looked as if they were Chapped. He started back to take the next Car, when he ran plump into an Old Friend from Memphis. The Acquaintance from the South said it was the Custom in his part of the Country when two Gentlemen met after a long Separation to pour a small Libation on the Altar of Friendship.

"You will excuse me if I don't refuse," said Hubby, and the two began to look around for a Place with Potted Ferns in the window.

As they laid their Breast-Bones against the metallic Hand-Rail, Hubby saw a Vision of a Lady with Auburn Hair. She was watching the Cars unload at the Corner. There was what you might term a Baleful Gleam in her Eye, and she was beginning to tap the Floor with one Tootsie. Those who understand the Matrimonial Code know that when a Lady with Zaza Tresses begins to telegraph with one Foot, then is the Time to climb a Tree. Hubby did not mention the Vision to his Friend from Memphis. He did not believe in telling his Troubles to an innocent Third Party.

The Man from Memphis ordered two Juleps. The Julep is built in a tall Vase. It consists of a leafy Roof Garden superimposed on a Display of Small Fruit, and whole underlaid with a Nansen Ice-Floe. Hubby had to take off his Hat in order to crawl through the Mint and get to the Beverage. As he looked at the fading Sunlight through the Kaleidoscope of Prismatic Flashes and Blushing Cherries, the Picture of Mabel with her Face against the Pane faded away and he beheld 10,000 stareyed Sirens in White, all singing "Dixie." He felt a great Love for the Southland welling up in his Heart.

So he told the Barkeep to put the Basket of Melons on the Ice and get busy with two more of the same.

He took Memphis by the Hand and said that Mason and

Dixon's Line was only a Memory. He wished to propose a Toast—to Sunny Tennessee, brightest Gem in the Diadem of States, the Home of Fair Women and Brave Men.

After the second Julep he told the Barkeep to take the Melons out and feed them to the Cat and to order up a Carriage with two Drivers. On Second Thought he decided to take the Melons along to throw at the Arc Lights in order to prove that the North and the South were One and Indivisible.

Hubby arrived home at 2 a.m. carrying the Handle of the Basket. When she opened up on him, he proved to her that he would have been there at 6.15 if she had not asked him to purchase all those Supplies.

Moral: *Usually the Woman is to Blame.*

The Fable of The Good Fairy of the Eighth Ward and the Dollar Excursion of the Steam-Fitters

Monnyhan lived right up in the City where they try to put Houses on one Lot.

The Name of the Thoroughfare was Kidd Street. It was in the Eighth Ward, just off Cinders avenue. There was a swell View of the Gas House and the Residents might have seen the Bottling Works and the Dump if it hadn't been for the Foundries in between.

Mr. Monnyhan worked in a Blast Furnace where they did not provide Electric Fans for the Help. When Summer came he never had to worry about his Polo Pony, and the Problem of getting a good Butler for the Country House did not give him a moment's Uneasiness. Mr. Monnyhan was one of the Plain People. He wiped his Mouth on the Back of his Hand, and when he saw a Man in Duck Trousers he had Murder in his Heart.

Shortly after the Whistle blew, Mr. Monnyhan would

show up in Kidd Street, dragging one Foot after the other, the Prosperity Dinner Pail in one horny Mitt and his Coat over his Arm. He would collapse on the Step with a Moan of Relief. Then he would call for his Evening Paper and read about Summer Styles for Well-Dressed Men.

After Supper he and the other Toilers along the Row would come out to the Front Stoops and peel off until they were comfortable, no matter what the *Ladies' Home Journal* said. The Children playing in the Street wore Rational Costumes. Sometimes a Foreigner came along and played on a Street Piano. The German at the Corner did a great Bucket Trade. After Mr. Monnyhan and his Neighbors had Rolled the Rock and Chased the Duck and Hurried the Can for several Pints of the White Suds they would feel almost as well off as the Rich.

Mrs. Monnyhan had a Grudge against Kidd Street. She was full of pipey Ambitions that did not fit in with Papa's Saturday Night Envelope. When she read about some New York Family going away on a Yacht and taking $10,000 worth of Ice along, she would feel Envious. The Monnyhans got most of their Ice in the Winter Time. Sometimes she would look out at the two lonesome Trees in Kidd Street and wish that her Husband was an unpopular Stock-Jobber instead of an honest Workingman. Mrs. Monnyhan loved to read about who was Entertaining at Newport and what to wear at the Races. She used to figure out what kind of speckled Horses she would drive to her Private Hack, if she should go out in the Alley some day and pick up a Million Dollar Bill. She spent a lot of Money in this way.

Mr. Monnyhan was a Home Body. He asked nothing better than an Al Fresco Evening on the Stoop, puffing his little Henry Clay and now and then burying his Face in the Growler.

But Mrs. Monnyhan had the Travel Microbe in her System. She wanted to take a Trip into the Country. Her Husband advised her to go over to the Park if she wanted to see some Grass, but she said that a real Outing meant at least 40 Miles on the Steam Cars. And she kept nagging Monnyhan.

One night the Good Fairy of the Eighth Ward came and perched on the Instalment Bedstead and spoke to Monnyhan as follows: "Your Side-Partner will never be happy until she gets that Ride to the Country. Next Sunday the Steam-Fitters' Protective Association gives a Dollar Excursion. I think it will help some if you give her enough Recuperation in one Day to last her all Summer."

Mr. Monnyhan acted on the Tip. His Wife was tickled to know that they were going. She loaded a Basket with Lunch and laid out her best Things.

On Sunday Morning the Monnyhans put on their heavy Clothing and started for the Station. The Sun got an Early Start. It was a hot, gummy Day—just the kind for an Excursion.

On the Railway Platform stood about One Thousand in their Sunday Best, slowly Cooking. The Monnyhans worked their way into the Pack. Every Person in that Crowd seemed to be radiating Heat like a Parlor Stove.

It was a sure-enough Sunday Bunch. There was Hiney Blotz with the Badge and the Pale Cigar. He was putting Finger Marks on the dove-colored Basque of Jimpsy, the pale Mechanic of the Commercial Hotel. Also there was Mike the Bite, with his regular Rollopozarium, who was Calcimined to a creamy white and chewing Pepsin Gum in two-four Time. And the Queen with the Satin Slippers and the gold Bridge-Work in her Teeth. Was she on hand with Clarence and his Patent Leathers?

Mrs. Monnyhan was looking for Society and she got her Dollar's Worth right on the Jump.

She was right next to a Stout Lady in white, who carried a Small Child, probably five weeks old. A very young Baby that is broken out with the Heat loves to get away on Sunday and have a Time with the Steam-Fitters. On the other side was a Gay Dog with a Red Handkerchief around his Neck and a Japanese Fan in his upper Coat Pocket. No Sunday Excursion is complete without this Boy.

The Cars had been standing in the Yards since 4.30, soaking up Heat. There were not enough Seats for all, so Mr. Monnyhan put the two Children in the Coal-Box, while he and the Pleasure-Seeker sat behind a Couple that talked Baby Talk. The Woman had artificial Cherries on her Hat and the Man smelled of Musk. Then somebody began to sing "A Bird in a Gilded Cage," and others started in to open up Lunch and throw Egg-Shells on the Floor. The Humorist who puts his Head out of the Window to Josh those at the different Stops was present in Numbers. Also the rollicking Youth who keeps tramping up and down the Aisles.

The Train ran for 6 Miles and then backed into a Siding at a Gravel Pit and waited for a Freight. The Excursion Train waits for Everything.

Mrs. Monnyhan had a Clinker in her Eye and Mr. Monnyhan's Collar was done for, so he thought it was about time to say something. He said he was glad he wasn't back at Home with his Coat and Vest off and a Dish of Hops in front of him. He thought that would be Miserable. Mrs. Monnyhan was still Game. She told him to wait until they were in the Country.

Along about Noon the Train pulled up near a Tree and somebody said they had arrived at the Grove. So they all piled out and stood around in the tall Timothy, waiting for something to happen.

Out in the Country if there is a Piece of Ground that cannot be farmed, they call it a Picnic Park and let the Stock run in it. The Monnyhans found themselves up against one of these bluff Groves. There was not enough Shade to go around. They had to take Turn About standing under the Tree. And if you didn't like the Place, you had to stay just the same, until the Train was ready to pull out.

The only Amusement was doing the Pivot Waltz with the

Heads together. That is no Entertainment for any one past twenty-eight, so the Monnyhans cut it out.

It was a long Day with nothing to see except the Track, the Rag-Weeds and a lot of Spoons who held on to one another for fear of losing a Good Thing.

The Train was seven hours in getting back, and by that time the Monnyhans were a Sight. It would not have been a regular Sunday Excursion if some Gentleman had not smashed another Gentleman for insulting his Lady. Mrs. Monnyhan fainted and dropped her Wild Flowers, and by the time she came to they were all over the Shop, knee-deep.

Late at Night the Monnyhans arrived at Kidd Street. To Mrs. Monnyhan those two dusty Trees were a Bower of Eden. She had taken enough Vacation to do her for quite a Spell. She wanted to get into the House and make a few Quick Changes and take a Long Breath.

So when they were back on their own Door-Step where they could shed their Garments and catch the Breeze from the Switch Yards, they realized that Kidd Street was an earthly Paradise.

Now, when Mrs. Monnyhan needs Recreation, she shakes a Nickel out of Willie's Bank and flags a Trolley.

Moral: *Be it ever so humble, there's no place like Home when it comes to Wearing what you like.*

The Fable of the All-Night Seance & The Limit That Ceased to Be

Four reputable Business Men sat down at the Green Baize to flirt with the Goddess of Fortune for one Hour, no more, no less. The Married Men did not want to go Home too early for fear that it would be too much of a Shock to their Wives.

These four Good Fellows may be designated as Adams, Brown, Collins and Davis, for fear the Children get hold of the Book. They were up in Adams' Room. Some one remarked that it was the mere Shank of the Evening—just the Fringe of the Night, as it were—and it seemed a Shame to pull for Home while so many other and more attractive Resorts were still open. So Adams brought out the necessary Tools and the four Comrades squared away.

It was to be a Gentleman's Game. No one at the Table wanted to take Money out of a Friend's Pocket. They put on an easy Limit of 10 Cents, so that no one could win or lose enough to Hurt. They had to make it an Object in order to keep their Blood in Circulation, but it was agreed that one fleeting Hour of 10-Cent Limit would not make or break any one. And it was positively understood and agreed that when the Cuckoo Clock hooted for Eleven O'clock, that was to be the Signal. Adams had been out the Night before with a Bad Man from Council Bluffs, and he wanted to make up a few Hours of Slumber. Brown had to figure on a Contract next Day, and he needed Eight Hours so as to show up with a Clear Head. Collins said he had a couple of Black Marks standing against him and if he didn't get in by Midnight, he might lose his Latch-Key. Davis said he was glad they were going to make it a Brief Session as the Electric Light hurt his Eyes. It seemed that not one had more than an Hour to spare.

It was a beautiful Get-Away. All the Stacks were the same size, neatly built up into Stand-Pipes of Red, White and Blue. The Cards riffled smoothly and the Dove of Peace seemed to hover over the Round Table. Each Man lighted an eight-inch Perfecto and got it slanted up so as to keep the Smoke out of his Eyes. He was feeling Immense because he counted on pulling out about Five Bones and buying a Hat with it.

Inasmuch as they were playing in Adams' Room and he was providing all the wet and dry Provisions, they felt at Liberty to jounce him. A Host is not supposed to act Peevish, no matter what they do to him. So what they did to Adams was a Plenty. It was only measly little Child's Game with a

Come In of Two call Five and a Blue Seed for the Outside Bet, but when two of them got Adams in between them and started the Whip-Saw, they left him with nothing but Whites. He died like an Outcast with three Type-Writers clutched in his Salary Hook.

He touched up the Bone Yard in a low, injured Tone of Voice and they could notice the Gloom curdling on his side of the Table. In a few Moments he tried to Get Back by making it Expensive to Draw. Davis picked up two Cards and filled a Straight and he lit on Mr. Bluffer all spraddled out. It was about this time that Adams began to get Red around the Ears. He told them to be careful where they dropped their Ashes, as the Rug they were sitting on was a genuine Bokhara and had stood him more than Two Hundred. They asked him if he was Sore, and he said he was not, but he hated to sit in with a Farmer who would hold up Three, open in the Middle, and then Fill. Any one who would do that ought to be Arrested. Davis remarked that their Host was an Imitation Sport who ought to be out playing Mumblety-Peg or Croquet. Davis had a long Breastwork of Plush in front of him and he was full of Conversation. He told Adams that if they injured the Rug he would buy another.

In the meantime the Short Hand had crept up toward XI. Davis kept calling Attention to the Fact that the Time was just about up. He wanted to get his Velvet and Dig. The Electric Light was hurting his Eyes worse than ever.

But when the Hour struck, Adams was just beginning to be keen for Trouble. He told them to forget the Clock. He threw the Johan Deck into the Grate, broke a fresh Pack, walked around his chair three times, took off his Coat and gave Fair Warning that all Boys and Cripples must get back of the Ropes. He rung in a new Rule than any one who bet less than 50 Cents would be considered a Gazabe. He put in a Patent Corkscrew for a Buck and said it called for a Jack Pot every time it came out with the Ante. He hoped that all of the Old Ladies and the Safe Players would dust the Cracked Ice out of their Laps and get Busy. He said if they tried hard they could get Action for their Money on something less than Threes.

Of course, they had agreed to chop off at Eleven, but they could not play Quitter on their Host while he was so deep in the Hole, so they all came down to their Shirt Sleeves and got ready for Rough Work. They began to Edge with the Colored Beans and Friendship ceased. Adams had a Run of Luck and he crowded it. Every time he skun his First Set and found it promising, he raised them out of their Chairs. It was a Half Dollar per Throw and somebody was thrown every Deal. Before long he had them Buying, and Brown had opened a Tab with the Bank.

Adams began to hum a Popular Air, just to show that he could Gamble without losing his Temper. He had All Kinds corded up in front of him and he was exceeding Blithe. He said he was going to buy some nice Etchings for his Room and put in an Ice-Box and have everything Right in case a few Friends dropped in like this. Then he glanced up at the Clock and said that probably they had better make it Midnight. At this the other three let out a Roar that would have been a Credit to Niagara. They said they were going to Hang On until they got Revenge. He explained that somebody had to quit Loser and besides, they couldn't sit up all Night. The Doctor had told him to get plenty of Sleep. They scoffed at him and told him to get a Hot Brick and put his Feet on it.

Brown arose and removed his flowered Waistcoat, rolled up his Sleeves and said they would let up on Fooling and begin in Earnest. They would play nothing but Jacks and it would cost One Dollar to Associate. With that they closed in an every Man was playing so near to his Shirt Bosom that he had to back off to read his Hand. The Light Conversation had died away. It was now a Case of getting the Heart's Blood. They talked in low, sick-room Whispers and eyed one another stealthily. Each of the four wondered if the Game was absolutely on the Square.

Along about 2 o'clock after the Luck had been see-sawing, Brown had four Treys and refused to take Cards. Two Full Hands came out against him and that was what led up to the Slaughter. When a Person stands Pat, it is the crafty Supposition that he has a Flush or a Straight. To hold the Extra Card as a Blind for Fours is justly regarded as an Act of Low Cunning. When the Smoke and Dust cleared away, Brown had everything in sight and was beginning to Yawn slightly and look at his Watch. The others were drawing on the Bank and telling what they might have done if the Cards hadn't come just as they did.

Adams had been Cleaned properly, and he was so Mad he was breathing through his Nose. He produced his Bank-Book to show that he was Good for any Amount, and then he abolished the Limit and announced that he was out for Gore and would show no Quarter.

Then the Game settled down to the Kind in which somebody lays $14 on a Pair of Sevens and gets whooped $9 by some other Desperado holding Nines, and nobody bats an Eyelash.

At 4 o'clock Brown, who was still intrenched behind his Earning, suggested that they play one Round of Jack Pots for Five Bucks and then settle up. This was reluctantly agreed to. In this Grand Finale some tall Hands were dealt and they didn't do a Thing to Brown. So he called for just one more Round and everybody locked Horns and began all over again.

At 6 o'clock when the Hot Sunlight fell athwart the Table the Room resembled a Roustabout Bar-Room. Four Haggard Beings, scantily Clad, sat at the Table and weakly endeavored to Bump one another. Adams was out a Month's Salary and was Dead on his Feet. Brown had worked like a Dog all night and had nothing to show for it except a Head and a Debit of $3.50. Collins had most of the Chips, but he would have given a Thousand to get out of going Home and facing Pet. Davis had been running the Bank, and he never will know how he came out. He had two Envelopes covered with

Marks, and after the others Cashed In, he didn't have any Money with which to redeem his own Checks. He asked what he had better do, and no one answered. They had Troubles of their own.

After they left and Adams put his Head under the Faucet, he said he was going to swear off on making his Room a Hang-Out for Sharks. And when they were safely outside, they agreed that Men with Homes ought to keep away from the Rounder Element. And everybody said "Never Again."

Moral: *Play Muggins, and then you will be glad to Quit at any time.*

The Fable of The Good People Who Rallied to the Support of the Church

A Congregation needed Money for repairing the Church, so the Women got together and decided to hold a Raspberry Festival. Sister Frisbie invited them to come and Carouse on her Front Lawn. Some 22 Members of the Flock flew out and bought a few Things to Wear, the Outlay for washable Finery running to about $8 per Head.

Mr. Frisbie got $9 worth of Chinese Lanterns and strung them around. He wanted to do the Thing up Brown so as to get a Puff in the Weekly. The Paper came out and said that the Frisbie Front Yard with its Myriad Twinkling Lights was a Veritable Fairy-Land. That kind of a Notice is worth $9 of anybody's Money.

Mr. Frisbie and three other Pillars of the Church devoted $7 worth of valuable Time to unloading Tables and Camp-Stools.

The Women Folks ruined $14 worth of Complexion working in the hot Kitchen to make Angel Food and Fig Cake.

On the Night of the Raspberry Orgy the Public Trampled down $45 worth of Shrubbery.

When it came time to check up the Linen and Silverware

it was found that $17 worth of Spoons with Blue Thread tied around them had been lost in the Shuffle.

The Drip from the Candles ruined $29 worth of Summer Suits and Percale Shirt-Waists.

Four Children gorged themselves and each was tied in a True Lover's Knot with Cholera Morbus before another Sunrise. The Doctor Bills footed up $18.

After clearing the Wreck, paying the Drayman and settling for the Ice Cream and Berries, it was discovered that the Church was $6.80 to the Good. So everybody said it was a Grand Success.

Moral: *Anything to avoid dropping it in the Basket.*

The Fable of Woman's True Friend & The Hopeful Antique

The Beauty Doctor sat in her Pink Reception Room hoping that she resembled her Lithographs. Her Income was a Dollar every time she took a Full Breath. She got it by selling Freckle Food and a Preparation for getting rid of Moles, called Moline. Her hot Specialty was to Calcimine the Has-Beens and feed them a little Ginger and send them into the Arena looking like Vassar Girls. It did not take her long to put an Extension on an Eye-Brow, and she could provide a Blush for those who had been going to Card Parties so long that they had forgotten how to Blush. When she got after a Wild Hair the Hair simply threw up both Hands and quit. In a little Folder entitled "How to Fool Everybody except those who live in the Same House," she had proved that there was no Reason why a Girl of 60 should not look 19 if she put on enough Shellac and kept out of the Light.

The Beauty Doctor had seen many a Derelict float in for a new Coat of Armor Plate, but the Nobody's Darling that wafted in this Day established a Record. She was something like Poultry. That is, if she carried any Adipose, it did not show in her Face or Feet. And she wouldn't have torn under the Wing. She had a Bird's-Eye Maple Complexion and wore one of these Gowns that you get by measuring yourself with a String and sending Two Dollars. Without saying anything in Disparagement of her Private Character or denying that she may have been kind to her Relations, it may be added that she resembled a Daily Hint from the Short Timber.

"I saw your Card in the Bee-Keepers' Bazaar, and I have decided to back in for a few Repairs," said the Visitor. "If you can build me a Set of Curves the same as I see in the Cigarette Pictures and cause my Hair to Bush out and hang to the Belt Line the same as it used to in 1882, and give me some perfumed Dope that will restore a Peaches and Cream Complexion on or before May 1st, I will do the Generous Thing by you and pay Seven Dollars."

The Beauty Doctor seldom took the Count, but this was one of the Times. "My Private Secretary will take charge of your Case," she said faintly, and then she went into another Apartment and lay down.

The Private Secretary was the Last Resort. He had no Conscience. For two seasons he had been a Cloak Salesman. "Surely you have not come here for Treatment," he said, smiling at the Caller. "You have the Shape that they are raving about in Paree this Spring, and we could not improve your general Tint no matter how many Coats we used. The quiet and unobtrusive Elegance of your Get-Up, combined with what Nature has so generously parcelled out to you, makes it unnecessary to attempt any Alterations. All that you need to do is to retain intact your present Category of Superlative Charms. This you can manage by a careful Perusal of our Book: 'How to stay Pretty.' It comes to Ten Louies."

So she had the Volume wrapped up and went away tickled.

Moral: *The only Ones who need Patching are those who Think they need it.*

The Fable of The Day's Work & The Morning After

Promptly at 7.30 the Alarm Clock went off. The Rounder sat on the Edge of his Bed and wondered if there was Anything in it. His Tongue felt like a Rug. He was afraid to work his Face for fear it would Crack.

He took a Cold Plunge, rubbed some Pepper Sauce in his Hair, drank a Quart of Hot Water, gargled a Patent Preparation warranted to kill the Maroon Taste, and by that Time he was able to look at his Watch and realize that nobody in the whole World truly Loved him. He did not seem to have any keen Craving for Breakfast, so he drank two large ruby-red Cocktails, smelling like Furniture Polish, just as an Appetizer. After he got them placed he sat at the Window for a while, watching the Landscape straighten itself out. He remembered that he had two or three Friends, after all, so he decided to give this Earth another Trial. Accordingly he ordered up as many Ham and Eggs as could be forced on one Platter and two Stacks of Buckwheat Cakes, and he kept on until he had extinguished the Cocktails.

At an Early Age the Rounder had read in McGizzick's Physiology that the Capacity of the Human Stomach is Three Pints. His Object in Life was to prove that McGizzick was away Off and must have got hold of a Youth's Size.

After the Rounder had smothered the Cocktails under 80 Cents' worth of Plain Food, he started for his Office, where he met a Drummer, who took him out to talk Business. They opened two or three Cold Bots and ate a few hillocks of Cottage Cheese, Souse, Dill Pickles, Radishes, Blutwurst and Rye Bread with Caraway in it, because they were Free. Then the Rounder excused himself because he had a Date for Luncheon. This light Repast consisted of Blue Points, Gumbo Soup, Fried Spring Chicken, Baked Potatoes, Cheese and other Food for the Gods floated to its Destination in a mixture of Ale and Stout, sometimes known as Liquid Buckshot. In the Afternoon our Hero went to his Club and played Pool, and whoever had it put on him had to buy what made Milwaukee famous for the Others. Along in the Middle of the Afternoon the McGizzick Theory did not have a Leg to stand on.

At Dinner Time he keyed up on Aqua Fortis and Bitters, which enabled him to take Nine Courses, with Red, White and Blue Irrigators to keep him Encouraged, and then four California Grapes for Dessert. By this Time, McGizzick, Author of the School Physiology, was a Liar by the Watch.

In the Evening the Rounder went to a Show. Between Acts he sauntered out with a few Western Gentlemen and seeped up frequent High Balls, accompanied by a little Snack of Oyster Crackers, the embalmed Herring known as the Blind Robin, Water Cress and Anchovies. After the Show they dropped in for their Broiled Lobster, Combination Salad, Welsh Rabbit and Nineteen Rounds of something to take. At a late Hour the Man who had demonstrated that McGizzick was an Ignoramus, went to his Brass Bedstead and lapsed into a State of Coma.

Next morning his Room was twisted. Some one had put a Bed of Live Coals under the Sheet. He felt as if he had swallowed a Steam Radiator and some one had gone down to repair it. He had a case of Bust-Head and a dry crackly Thirst. He sent for a Physician, and when the Learned Man came to make his Diagnosis, the Rounder said: "Doc, it's my own Fault. I ate some Grapes last Night."

Moral: *Avoid Fruit.*

The Fable of The Man Who Was Going to Retire

A Business Slave was pulling like a Turk so that his Wife could wear three Rings on every Finger. Also, he wanted to put aside something for a Rainy Day. He put it aside as if expecting another Deluge.

He always said that he was going to Retire when he had Enough. When he was 20 years old he hoped to amass $10,000. At 30 he saw that he would not be able to peg along on less than $100,000. When he was 40 he realized that a Man that didn't have a Million was little better than a Tramp. At 50 he wanted to make the Elkins-Widener Syndicate look like a band of Paupers.

At 60 he still promised himself that he would retire. Just as soon as he had cabbaged everything Getatable, then he was going to lie back in an Invalid Chair and read the 18,000 Books he had collected, but he had not found time to cut the Leaves.

In order to get ready for his Lay-Off he built a Home in the Country. He told the Architect to throw himself on something compared with which Windsor Castle would be a Woodman's Hut. He decided on a Deer Park, a Poultry Farm and Ancestral Oaks, so as to have something Ancestral.

He put up a Shack that reminded one of the State Capitol at Springfield. It was big enough for a Soldiers' Home. The Family consisted of himself and his Wife, and the Architect allowed them 19 Bath-Rooms apiece.

The Rugs and Tapestries cost $1.75 a Thread. Every Painting was fresh from the Salon and had the Cost-Mark attached to show that it was Good Goods.

When the Place was completed he handed the Business over to the Junior Partners and went out to Rest. He turned on all the Fountains and ordered the Birds to strike up. The Dream of his Life had come True. He had no Cares, no Responsibilities. All he had to do was sit there and watch the Grass grow.

He enjoyed it for nearly 25 minutes and then he began to Fidget, so he went and sat in the Marie Antoinette Room for a while and counted the Stripes in the Fresco. Afterward he took a Turn about the Grounds and came back and wondered if everything was running along all right at the Office.

"Gee, but this is Tame!" said the Retired Hustler. "I

think I'd better take a little Run into Town to be sure that the Under-Strappers are not making a Botch of it."

At 11 o'clock he was back at the Old Stand, hovering about like an Uneasy Spirit. He looked over the Correspondence and dictated a few Letters and got the Noise in his Ears and he began to feel Good again.

His Associates told him to clear out and play with the Deer and the Prize Chickens.

"I have been Associating with them all Morning," was the Reply. "They did not seem disposed to close any Contracts, so their Society palled on me. Besides, I have been looking around and see that you can't get along without me. Furthermore, it is all Tommy-Rot for a man of 68 and just entering the Prime of Life to talk of Retiring."

When the Reaper finally came the old Gentleman was found in the Tread-Mill but he was still counting on making use of the Country Place, next Year or possibly the Year after.

Moral: *One cannot Rest except after steady Practice.*

The Fable of The Bookworm and The Butterfly Who Went into the Law

Two Brothers started away to College at the same Time. Just before they boarded the Train, Pa led them aside and handed them some splendid Advice. He told them that they were now ready to mold their Futures. He said he wanted them to stay in of Evenings and Bone hard, and he hoped they would mind the Faculty and keep away from the Cigarette Fiends who play the Banjo and talk about Actresses. He wanted them to stand high in their Classes and devote their Spare Moments to Reading rather than to the Whimsies and Mimical Fooleries of a University Town.

William listened solemnly and promised to Behave.

Cholley fidgeted in his Chair and said it was nearly Train-Time.

So they rode away on the Varnished Cars, William reading about the Goths and Vandals and Cholley playing Seven Up with a Shoe Drummer from Lowell.

At the University William remembered what Pa had said, so he cooped himself up in his Room and became a Dig and soon enough was greatly despised as a Pet of the Professors. Cholley wore a striped Jersey and joined the Track Team and worked into the Glee Club. He went to his Room when all the other Places had closed up. Every Time a Show struck Town he was in the Front Row to guy the Performers and pick up some new Gags. He went calling on all the Town Girls who would stand for his Fresh Ways, and he was known as the best Dancer in the Ki Ki Chapter of the Gamma Oopsilon Greek Letter Fraternity. The Reports sent Home indicated that William was corralling the Honors in Scholarship and Cholley was getting through each Exam by the Skin of his Teeth, but he had been elected a Yell Captain and could do his 100 Yards in Ten Seconds Flat. Pa would write to Cholley now and then and tell him to Brace Up and give him a Hunch that Life was full of Sober Responsibilities and therefore he had better store his Mind with Useful Knowledge and Chop on all the Frivols and Fopperies, whereupon Cholley would write back that he needed Fifty by Return Mail to pay for Chemicals used in the Laboratory.

By the Time that both were Seniors, William had grown a fuzzy Climber in front of each Ear and was troubled with Weak Eyes. He always had a Volume of Kant under his Arm and seemed to be in a Brown Study as he walked across the Campus. Cholley kept himself Neat and Nobby and seemed always Cheerful, even though he had two or three Conditions to his Discredit and had only an Outside Chance of taking his Degree. He was Manager of the Football Team, and he had earned the affectionate Nickname of "Rocks." He was a great Hand to get acquainted with any

Girl who dared to show herself near the Halls of Learning and by constant Practice he had developed into a Star Chinner, so that he could Talk Low to almost any one of them and make her believe that of all the Flowers that ever bloomed she was the one and only $30,000 Carnation.

William kept away from Hops and Promenades because he remembered what Pa had said about the Distracting Influence of Fripperies and the Tittle-Tattle of Artificial Society. The only Girl he knew was a Professor's Sister, aged 51, with whom he was wont to discuss the Theory of Unconscious Cerebration. Then he would drink a Cup of Young Hyson Tea and go Home at 8.45 p.m. Cholley at about that Time would be starting out in his Primrose and Dockstader Suit to write his Name on Dance Cards and get acquainted with the Real Folks.

On Commencement Day William received the Cyrus J. Blinker Prize of a Set of Books for getting the Highest General Average of any one in the Class. Cholley just managed to Squeeze Through. The Faculty gave him a Degree for fear that if it didn't he might come back and stay another Year.

After they had graduated, Pa gave them another Talk. He said he was proud of William, but Cholley had been a Trial to him. Still he hoped it was not too late to set the Boy on the Right Track. He was going to put both of them into a Law Office and he wanted them to Read Law for all they were worth and not be lured away from their Work by the Glittering Temptations of Life in a Big City. William said he was prepared to Read Law until he was Black in the Face. Cholley said he wouldn't mind pacing a few Heats with Blackstone and Cooley now and then, if he found that he could spare the Time. The Father groaned inwardly and did not see much Hope for Cholley.

When the two Sons became Fixtures in the Office of an established Law Firm, William kept his Nose between the Leaves of a Supreme Court Report and Cholley was out in the other Room warming up to the Influential Clients and making Dates for Luncheons and Golf Foursomes.

Within three Months after they started at the Office, William had read all the Books in the Place and Cholley was out spending three weeks at the Summer Home of the President of a Construction Company, who was stuck on Cholley's Dialect Stories and liked to have him around because he was such a good Dresser and made it lively for the Women.

Out at this Country Place it happened that Cholley met a Girl who didn't know how much she was worth, so Cholley thought it would be an Act of Kindness to help her find out. When he sat out with her in the Cool of the Evening and gave her the Burning Gaze and the low entrancing Love Purr that he had practised for Four Years at the University, she stopped him before he was half finished, and told him that he need not work Overtime, because he was the Boy for Nellie. She said she had had him Picked Out from the Moment that she noticed how well his Coat set in the Back.

In one of the large Office Buildings of the City there is a Suite finished in Dark Wood. At a massive roll-top Desk sits Cholley, the handsome Lawyer, who is acquainted with all the Club Fellows, Society Bucks and Golf Demons. When a Client comes in with a Knotty Question, Cholley calls in a Blonde Stenographer to jot down all the Points in the Case. Then the Client departs. Cholley rings a Bell and Brother William comes out of a Side Room with his Coat bunched in the Back and his Trousers bagged at the Knees. His Cravat is tied on one Side only and he needs a Shave, but he is full of the Law. Cholley turns all the Papers over to him and tells him to wrestle with the Authorities for a few Days and Nights. Then William slips back into his Hole and Humps himself over the calf-bound Volumes while Cholley puts on his slate-colored Gloves and Top Coat and goes out to where Simpson is holding a Carriage Door open for him. He and Nellie take the air in the $2,200 Victoria that he bought with her Money and later in the Day

THE WILLING PERFORMER

they dine with the Stockson-Bonds and finish at the Theater.

Cholley often reflects that it was a great Piece of Foresight on Pa's part to counsel Studious Habits and Rigid Mental Discipline, for if William had not been a Grind at College probably he would not have proved to be such a Help around the Office, and although William gets the Loser's End of the Fees and is never Called on to make a Witty Speech at a Banquet given by the Bar Association, he has the Satisfaction of knowing that he is the Silent Partner of the best-dressed Attorney in Town and one who is welcome wherever he goes.

Moral: *There are at least two Kinds of Education.*

The Fable of The Crustacean Who tried to Find Out by Reading a Book

Once there was a Man who lived in the same Hall Bed-Room for 14 Years. It was a snug little Box-Stall. There were raspy Lace Curtains on the Windows. The Man used to scratch Matches on them. Also there were two Paintings. One was either a Landscape or a Marine, and the Second represented a Male Gazelle with his Hair combed the Way the Barber will comb it unless you stop him.

The Roomer would come Home about once a Day and climb over the Paste-Board Trunk and look out at the Roof of the adjoining House, and then decide to Go Out and stay as Late as possible. He ate at a Restaurant in which Tall Waitresses with Belladonna Eyes and False Frizzes showed a Partiality for the Customers who Waxed their Mustaches. He was accustomed to Bolt his Food, while some one named Gert leaned a Tray against him and entreated Laura in the Kitchen to Cut a Hot Mince and let the Fried Sweets come along with the Medium Sirline.

When he received his Biennial Bid to go around to some Private House he took his Chop-House Manners with him. He would feel around his Plate for the little Yellow Ticket with the Granulated Sugar caked on it, and perchance he would ask the Maid if she had an Evening Paper lying around loose.

He had formed certain Habits inseparable from the Rank Outsiders and the Hoi Bolloi. It was Second Nature for him to plant both Elbows on the Table and use the Celery as a Whisk Broom, and try to balance the Knife on the Fork, and spill some Salt on the Table-Cloth and write his Name in it with a Tooth-Pick. He needed a Check-Rein and Hobbles to hold him back in his Chair and keep him from Playing with the Table-Ware.

About the Time that he was 40 and a confirmed Reuben, he got in with the Rise in Industrials, and the Wave of

Prosperity carried him out of the Hall Bed-Room and landed him in a Suite that he called a Suit.

He crowded his Luck and Parleed his Bets. Things came his way and he decided that he might as well begin to Mingle with the Face Cards and make up for Lost Time. He had read in a Bitter Editorial somewhere that any one who had the Stuff could work the Open Sesame on the 400, and he was willing to relinquish a few Shares of Atchison Preferred in order to see his Name linked with those of the Butterflies of Fashion. He had noticed that every one Made Fun of the People in Society and tried to get Acquainted with them, and he was Willing to be a Member of the Despised Faction.

A Piano-Player who went right into the Best Houses, unless they happened to hear about it in Time, said he would Fix it for him. So the Hall Bed-Room Man had a lot of Clothes made with Silk Lining, whether it showed or not, for he was Determined to be the real Peruvian Doughnuts, and there wasn't a Thing to do.

He realized that he would have to get some Inside Information on Etiquette, Table Manners and Good Form, but he thought about three Lessons would put him in Condition to Saunter into any Drawing Room and set Everybody to Whispering about him.

There were just a few Points that he wanted to straighten out before he took his Header into the Swim. He had heard that a True Gentleman must or must not wear a Bob-Tailed Coat with a Tall Hat, but he could not remember which. Furthermore, he had a Dim Idea that any one wearing a Tuxedo would have to cut out the Tan Shoes or else have the Lorgnettes pointed at him. He had heard, also, that it was considered Rough Work to eat Peas with a Spoon, or possibly a Fork, or perhaps a Knife. So he always passed up the Petit Pois when any one was watching him, and merely ate a little Bread with a Fork, because that was a Cinch.

The Piano-Player had suggested to him in a roundabout

Way that any one who put a Napkin inside of his Collar or wore a striped Bow with Full Dress would be shell-roaded, and never to wear Yellow Gloves at a Ball, or it would be a Case of the Blue Wagon.

He found it was quite a Jump from a Hall Bed-Room and a Home-Cooked Meal for 25c. to the Society of Large Gloomy Ladies who used the Side of the Spoon instead of the End. He began to understand that he had shouldered quite a Contract when he tried to break away from the Herd and run forward with the Bell-Cows.

Still, he made a Flying Start. The Piano-Player worked him into a Dinner Party. The Hostess did not want to have just Thirteen at the Table, and that is how the Hall Bed-Room Man wedged in. He received his Invitation at 6.15, and at 6.45 he was on the Spot with a new Pair of Patent Leathers.

He noticed that he was the only Gentleman present who wore Opal Studs, with a Black Handkerchief folded across the Abdominal Region so as to produce a Dressy Effect. He feared that he was not as de Rigueur as some of the Boys that had been in the Game for a Season or more, and it Rattled him so that he used the Large Spoon for the Blue Points and the Coffee Spoon for the Potage. He tried to watch the Others to see which Implements to pick up next, but most of them were taking Desperate Chances, the same as he was. By the Time he reached Ice Cream he had no Tools left except a cute little Harpoon and something that looked like a Surgical Instrument.

He rather Tripped up on the Conversation too, for he had not learned to play Golf and never had been to see the Rogers Brothers. Once he thought he saw an Opening, and he offered to show his new $200 Watch, but every one started to Talk about something else, and the Piano-Player kicked him under the Table.

He went home from the Dinner wondering if he wouldn't do better on the Night Shift at the Glue Works than in the Front Row at a Function.

When a Woman sent him her Card with "Thursdays" written in the Lower Left Corner, he didn't know whether he should Write, Mail a Card, send Flowers, or regard it as an Effort on her part to make a Date.

He saw that there were a great many Fine Points in the Society Racket that were New Ones on him.

So he went out and bought a Little Book written by a Space Man living in a Stag Hotel, informing People how to Behave so as to give the Impression that they were Well-Bred, no matter what the Facts might be.

He went up to his Suite and read the Book and discovered that during the whole 40 Years of his life he never had done anything According to Hoyle.

He had been accustomed to carry his Laundry with him each Saturday Evening. The Book said that carrying a Bundle in the Street was a little worse than Sheep-Stealing, and almost as bad as beating a Crippled Child with a Mallet.

He nearly choked with Shame when he read that any one who played a combination of Frock Coat and low Derby was guilty of a Misdemeanor, and to omit the Stick or Umbrella was nothing short of a High Crime.

It said that all Vegetables should be carried on the Fork. He did not believe it could be done. He was no Equilibrist.

He read that Men must not wear Jewelry. He had always supposed that no Man could be out-and-out Genteel on anything less than 14 Carats.

Then there was something more about the Spoon. Any one leaving a Spoon in the Cup could be set down as a Boor, whatever that meant. And any one breaking Crackers into the Soup deserved to be Drawn and Quartered.

But what Stopped him was the Warning that no one drinking from the Saucer could be tolerated in the Best Circles. He wondered if a Man ought to Scald himself, merely to be Correct.

When he concluded the Book and perceived that he had invariably violated every Rule from A to Z, he knew that he did not belong, and never would, so he blew out the Gas, and they found Him there in the Morning.

Moral: *To insure Peace of Mind, ignore the Rules and Regulations.*

The Fable of The Skittish Widower Who Tried to Set Himself Back Some Thirty Years

Once there was a Self-Made Citizen who Manufactured a Patent Churn. He had been married for thirty-four Years and had three Children who were Grown Up and Settled. He had Grubbed along all his Life. In his Youth he never had gone High Rolling because he had been learning a Trade. His Compensation consisted of Board and Clothes and a Yarn Comforter every Christmas. After he got Married it was a Case of planting all the Small Change so as to be there with the Rent Money on the First.

In Time the Churn Maker got the Grape Vine Twist on Adversity and Won Out. He had all kinds of Collateral and they began to be Pleasant to him at the Bank. He could have written his Check for Six Figures, but he never did.

He continued to live in the same Modest Style and his Habits seemed to be Fixed. He never ordered any Hot House Grapes for fear they would spoil his Appetite for Prunes. He used a Bone Collar Button and a Ready-Made Bow Tie that fastened on with an Elastic.

One Day was the same as another to him. He would arise at half-past six and go out to feed the Horse and look at the Thermometer. Then he would have his Fried Steak and two Cups of Martha's Coffee, and start for the Factory to go through the Mail and try to put a Compress on the Pay Roll. The Women along that Street could set their Clocks by him, for he always came home to Dinner just at ten minutes past twelve. After he had disposed of the Roast Beef and Trimmings and had his Wedge of Pie, he would feed the Horse again and try to estimate how much longer the Coal was going to last. Then back to the Place where the Churns were made. At half-past five he would return for Supper. When they had Company they called it Tea. In the Evening, if there was no Grand Army Camp-fire or Prayer Meeting he would hold down a Rocking Chair in the Sitting Room. He seldom wore a Coat around the House. He had a Pair of Velvet Slippers, worked for him by his Daughter-in-Law, and when he put them on in the Evening he groaned with Satisfaction. He would sit and read Churn Literature until half-past nine, and then he would turn out the Cat, wind the Clock, fix the Damper on the Furnace and connect with the Feathers. At half-past six next Morning he was up to repeat the Routine.

After thirty-four Years of this, he found himself a Widower. For a Time he moped around by himself. The Blackest Clothes he could get were not half Black enough. Although he still lived at the House, he took his Meals out at a Boarding House conducted by a Lady who had driven her own Carriage at one time, and said so at every Meal.

He missed the Coffee, and the Pie did not taste right. It was still and lonesome in the Sitting Room. One Evening it was so Creepy around the House when he tried to read that he went out for a Walk. As he strolled it occurred to him that it had been Many Moons since he had taken the Night Air with any Regularity. It seemed rather strange to realize that if he wanted to he could stay out as late as the Owl Cars. For the first Time since his Bereavement he felt the Gloom lifting. He had to acknowledge that the sense of Liberty gave him a new kind of Thrill. His Better Judgment told him that inasmuch as he was his own Boss, and had Nobody to check him up, he might as well Perk up and not overdo the Pining Away. So he kept on Walking until he came to the Temperance Billiard Hall, where he rang in on some Students from the Shorthand College and learned to play Bottle Pool. Once in a while he would give a Quick Start and have an Impulse to get a Move on himself, for the

Knowledge that he was as Free as the Air had not thoroughly soaked in on him as yet.

In a few Evenings he overcame this Jumpy Feeling and stopped looking at Clocks. He learned to make Follow Shots and play for Position and leave a hard Set-Up for the next Player. When he had Chalk all over his Clothes and was banging out Three Cushion Shots to keep from being Stuck, he began to feel like One of the Boys.

He was in the Clover Pasture for the first time, and he could not refrain from Rolling Over and Kicking Up. He got a lot of new Clothes made at a Tailor Shop, and began to smell of Musk and wore a Pair of Yellow Gloves. Then he bought a Trotter and a Piano-Box Buggy with Cushion Tires, and he was seen walking up and down in front of Millinery Stores. He wore these Hot Stripes on his Shirt, and he had a dove-colored Fedora Hat, such as a fly Bartender wears on Sunday.

But he took an overdose of the Elixir of Youth when he had his Hair and Whiskers dyed the color of India Ink. He wanted to make all the Women in Town think he was going on Twenty-seven. The Dye began to wear off and the Crop had an Oxidized Appearance and was Gray around the Roots. He was a Fright, but he didn't think so.

His Children and the other Relatives worried a little, but they did not Discuss the Matter of having a Guardian appointed until the old Gentleman became all snarled up with a portly Amazon named Blanche. Blanche had been very Careless with her Husbands, and she could not tell, without looking over her Books, where she had left all of them. Her name was a Household Word around the Divorce Courts, and she moved every Month because she could not find a Neighborhood that was Refined enough to suit her.

Blanche was a large, creamy Blonde and came of a Swell Family somewhere in the South, but she had forgotten the Name of the Place.

When she tightened the Lasso on the Churn Manufacturer and prepared to give him the Strong Arm, one of his

Relatives sent out a General Alarm. His Daughter and his two Sons, who were naming Children after him and wondering how the Estate was to be divided, got the Family Lawyer, and the whole Posse tried to Split Out the rejuvenated War Horse and the buxom Divorcee.

They told him that she was an Adventuress with a Record that covered five or six States, and that all she wanted was his Roll. He said they must be Mistaken, because Blanche had Explained everything and told him in so many Words that he was the first Man she ever Loved right down to the Ground, and he would be just the same to her if he didn't have a Sou Markee.

Blanche knew that they were trying to sidetrack the Wedding, so when he came to see her again she sat on his Lap and told him he was free to Abandon her if he thought she was a Mercenary Girl, but the Minute he walked out of that Door, then nothing short of Prussic Acid would do for her. It was the First Time in her life she had known the Happiness of coming into the Life of a Good and Distinguished Man, and if he cast her aside and treated her as a Plaything—well, there would be a Piece in the Paper, that was all.

The Churn Maker might have known that nobody but Sandow could cast aside a Plaything weighing 180, but she had him believing anything when she stroked the Dye. It was a Fierce Line of Talk, but it went with him, for he had been sitting Indoors for thirty-four Years, and what he did not know about the Blanche Type would have filled many a Page. She had him Winging. While he was under the Influence of Knock-Out Drops or something else equally Potent, she spirited him away in a Hack and had him Married and signing Checks before the Detectives could Locate them.

As soon as she had him Roped and Thrown she had to hurry away to visit an Invalid Cousin in Washington. The Sight Drafts began to cut Scallops into his Bank Account, and the Churn Manufacturer found himself Guessing, although he received a Collect Telegram every Hour of the Day, telling him how she longed to see him again and to meet all Drafts and not believe anything he heard.

Then his Son got hold of him and began to beat it into him that he had been Played.

By the time the Lawyer got a Decree and fixed Blanche with the Hush Money and all the Fees had been settled, the Wallet of the Churn Manufacturer looked as if it had been put through a Wringer. He let his Whiskers grow out Gray again, and whenever he went out Walking they sent one of the Grandchildren along to take care of him.

Moral: *The older the easier.*

The Fable of How the Canny Commercial Salesman Guessed the Combination

A Country Merchant, sometimes known as the Man behind the Face, was sitting in his Prunery one Day when a Drummer came in to sell him a lot of Goods that he didn't need. As the Drummer closed the Door behind him and put on his copyrighted Smile, the Temperature of the Room sank about eight Degrees. There were no "Welcome" Mottoes on the Wall, and when the Drummer gazed into the rugged Map he realized that he was up against it.

But he was accustomed to warming up these Cold Propositions. He asked, "How's Tricks?" and was told that the entire Works, Government and all, was going to the Bow-wows. Thinking to dispel the Gloom, he told two of the Latest, and although they were Corkers and had caused many a Yokel to fall off the Cracker-Barrel, they never feazed old Mournful Ike. It was not his Day to be jollied. Then the Drummer switched and tried the Sympathetic Dodge. He said that Collections had been a little Slack, but he looked for Better Times as soon as the Farmers began to move their Crops. But the Face couldn't see a Glimmer of Hope.

The wise Drummer always has two old Stand-Bys that he brings out when all else has failed, viz., Politics and Religion. He decided to take a Chance.

"What do you think?" he said. "I had an awful Argument on the Train with a Chump who claimed that there was nothing in this Predestination Business."

"Then you believe in Infant Damnation, do you?" asked the Storekeeper.

"Sure," was the reply.

"You can send me a Berrel of New Orleens Molasses, ten Kits of Mackerel, seven Gross of Canned Peaches, and a Caddy of Oolong," said the Storekeeper.

Moral: *One smell of Brimstone makes the whole World kin.*

The Fable of the Old Fox and the Young Fox

After he had lived in Town for many Years and had come to know the Animals and their Ways, even to the occasional Running Amuck of the Bulls and Bears, the Old Fox had gathered to himself a few Hard Lessons which he set down for the Instruction and Betterment of Fox, Jr. One Day he took his Young One into the Private Office for a Session of Fatherly Advice.

"I have a few Nuggets of Truth," said the Old Fox, showing some loose Scraps of Paper on which he had written. "I hesitate to offer them, for, if I remember correctly, the Member of our Family who was Best Posted on Business Epigrams went under as far back as 1873. Still, some of these may help you. The Work of turning them out has been a pleasurable Respite from my ordinary Routine. Proverbs are easily Manufactured, my Son. They are Self-Evident Truths, blooming in the Garden of Inexperience.

Those which happen to be the right Length to fit into Copy-Books are most likely to Endure. Forty Years Ago I was competent to turn out Dozens of Maxims and Proverbs, each glistering with Truth. You are in the Fluff of Youth, while I am marked with Gray, yet doubtless you could give me Cards and Spades in the Making of Precepts for the Guidance of the Immature. The dear little Girls in the Grammar-Schools write Essays in which Mighty Conclusions are linked together end to end, Emerson Fashion. With one Reading of Poor Richard and some timely Inspiration from Rochefoucauld and Hazlitt, any Upstart may set down our Common Weaknesses and catalogue a full Set of Danger Signals. The Letter of Advice has been the easiest Form of Composition from the time of Chesterfield. However, in preparing you to go out and be of the City Tribe, and come Home each Night with your Brush unbedraggled and your cool, smooth Nose unmarked by Scratches, I flatter myself that I have omitted the usual Rigamarole of Weighty Instructions, my Experience having convinced me that the machine-made Proverb is seldom brought out except to be Misapplied."

"Thank you, Father," said the Young Fox. "I am glad that you have saved yourself the Trouble of formulating the Generalities for which the Rising Generation is always prepared. I have fixed up for my own Use a Set of Rules which, doubtless, is more Comprehensive and Beautiful than anything you could put together at your Time of Life."

Saying which, the Young Fox showed a pretty Morocco-Leather Booklet, made to fit the Waistcoat Pocket, in which he had written many meaty Paragraphs, the Substance of the same having been deduced from what he had read of the Struggle for Existence.

"Read a few Selections," said the Old Fox, with a Tolerant Smile. "I love to hear the resounding Conclusions of an Oracle."

"But I am not an Oracle," said the Young Fox, Modestly. "I am not even an Authority. I am only a bright Juvenile who has sorted out the Essentials for Success and set them down neatly with my Fountain-Pen."

"Do not flatter yourself that I credit you with the Authorship of any of the Matter contained in your little Book," said the Old Fox. "We do not intend to Plagiarize, but all of us absorb our pet Proverbs from the Text-Books, the learned Monthlies, and the Editorial Page. We paraphrase Benjamin Franklin, and put Two and Two together to make Four, and change a Preposition, and presto! the Old Saw seems to be a new Truth evolved without Help or Suggestion. No doubt you have written in your little Guide to Life that a Youthful Frugality insures Comfort throughout the Declining Years, and a Good Name is better than Riches, and to be sure you are Right before you go Ahead."

"Not in those Words, I assure you," said the Young Fox, somewhat testily. "It is true, however, that I have composed certain General Directions in favor of Honesty, Temperance, Economy, Punctuality, Candor, Politeness, and Business Caution."

"All Men declare for these Admirable Traits in their Pocket Note-Books," said the Old Fox. "And no sooner is the Ink dry than they are led astray by the Caprice of Small Happenings. The Trouble with a world-wide Maxim or a great bulky Truth is that it does not dovetail nicely into the Exigencies of a Petty Case. Here at the beginning of the Twentieth Century, my Son, when all Endeavor is being subdivided and specialized, a Technical Instruction under a Sub-Head has more Practical Value than a huge Proverb that has come bumping down the Ages. The Health Officer who tells you in a terse Bulletin to boil your Drinking-Water does you an Actual Service and the Results are immediate, as the Bacilli can testify. But you might have to hunt around all Day without finding an Opportunity to make use of Mr. Emerson's tremendous Suggestion, "Hitch your Wagon to a Star." I am not poking Fun at the Large Rules for Conduct, but I beg to remark that very often you will find that they are Shelf Ornaments instead of

Working-Tools kept bright by Use. Like the other Classics of our Literature, they are profoundly respected and seldom Utilized. What you need now, my Son," continued the Old Fox, "is a Set of Proverbs, Precepts, and Maxims brought up to Date and peculiarly adapted to an Era of Horseless Carriages, Limited Trains, Colonial Extension, Corners in Grain, the Booming of New Authors, Combinations of Capital, the Mushroom Growth of an Aristocracy of Wealth, and the Reign of Tailor-Made Clothes. A Majority of the Points to which I shall call your Attention may seem to be Frivolous and hardly worth while, but, as I have already intimated, it is the small Rule, made to fit the Individual Instance, that proves most valuable in the Long Run. Years ago I made a silly little Rule, as follows: 'Never extend Credit to any one who wears a Blue Necktie.' Childish, say you? Perhaps, but it has saved me Thousands of Dollars. If you will give sincere Heed to what I have inscribed here, you may be able to duplicate my magnificent Career."

Fox, Jr., took the Slips of Paper and read as follows:

1. Get acquainted with the Heads of Departments and permit the Subordinates to become acquainted with you.

2. Always be easily Familiar with those who are termed Great in the Public Prints. They are so accustomed to Deference and Humility, it is a positive Relief to meet a jaunty Equal.

3. As soon as you get an Office of your own, put in a Private Exit, marked, "Escape in Case of a Dear Friend with an Invitation to Dinner."

4. The first Sign of Extravagance is to buy Trousers that one does not need. Every Young Man on a Salary should beware of the Trousers Habit.

5. If you were Cut Out to be a homely American, with a preference for Turnips and Tea Biscuit, do not attempt to Live It Down. The most pathetic Object this year is the Man who wants to be a Degenerate and can't quite make it.

6. A Bird in the Hand may be worth Two in the Bush,

but remember also that a Bird in the Hand is a positive Embarrassment to one not in the Poultry Business.

7. Do not give Alms promiscuously. Select the Unworthy Poor and make them Happy. To give to the Deserving is a Duty, but to help the Improvident, Drinking Class is clear Generosity, so that the Donor has a Right to be warmed by a Selfish Pride and count on a most flattering Obituary.

8. There is Everything in a Name. A Rose by any other Name would Smell as Sweet, but would not cost half as much during the Winter Months. This means that you should get a Trade-Mark and keep it displayed on the Bulletin Boards.

9. Never try to get into Society, so-called. Those who Try seldom get in, and if they do edge through the Portals they always feel Clammy and Unworthy when under the Scrutiny of the Elect. Sit outside and appear Indifferent, and after a while they may Send for you. If not, it will be Money in your Pocket.

10. All the Apostles of Repose and the Mental Scientists tell the Business Slave to avoid Worry, but an old Trader's Advice is to Worry until you have had enough of it and then do something Desperate.

11. Never write when you can Telegraph, and in Wiring always use more than Ten Words. This is the Short-Cut to being regarded as a Napoleon. The Extra Words cost only a few Cents, but they make a Profound Impression upon the Recipient and give the Sender a Standing which could not be obtained by an Expenditure of Four Dollars for a Birthday Gift. A Man never feels more Important than when he receives a Telegram containing more than Ten Words.

12. Remember that the latest Outline for a Business Career is to Rush and Bustle and Strain to accumulate enough Money to pay your Expenses to Carlsbad or Southern California after you have dropped from Overwork. The only Failure is the one who Breaks Down without having got together his Recuperation Fund.

13. An Ounce of Prevention is worth a Pound of Cure and costs more. Don't attempt to prevent Trouble or you will

lose your Eyesight watching so many Corners at the same time. Wait until Trouble comes and then consult a Specialist.

14. When a Man is in a New Town his Prospects are determined (1) by the class of Hotel at which he is registered, (2) by his Wardrobe, (3) by the Style of his Business Card, and (4) by the Manner of his Address.

15. A Rolling Stone gathers no Moss and therefore will not be derided as a Moss-Back. Roll as much as possible.

16. If you must Economize, dispense with some of the Necessities. You can bear up under the Realization that the Gas Company knows of your keeping the Jets turned low, but if you go out of a Café followed by the Reproachful Gaze of a Waiter who regards you as Stingy, you will feel Small and Unhappy for Hours afterward and your Work will suffer.

17. It has been accepted as a Law that there can be no absolute Waste of Energy, but you will be putting the Law to a Severe Test if you permit yourself to be drawn into a political Controversy on a Sleeping-Car with a Stranger who wears a wide Slouch-Hat.

18. The Shorter the Hours, the Larger the Income. Don't get into the Habit of putting in Long Hours or you may be set down into a permanent Subordinate Position.

19. When you believe that you love a Young Woman so earnestly that you will have to Marry her, take a Long Ride on the Cars to find out if the Affection endures while you are Travelling. The Beauty of this Test is that if you really Love her, you never will start on the Trip by yourself.

20. If you expect to be a popular After-Dinner Speaker, don't attempt to work at anything else. That is a sufficiently large Contract for one brief Existence.

21. If you take care to Pronounce correctly the Words usually Mispronounced, you may have the Self-Love of the Purist, but you will not sell any Goods.

22. Never accuse a Man of being Lazy. There is no such thing as Laziness. If a Man does not go about his work with Enthusiasm, it means that he has not yet found the Work

that he likes. Every Mortal is a Busy Bee when he comes to the Task that Destiny has set aside for him.

23. Early to Bed and Early to Rise is a Bad Rule for any one who wishes to become acquainted with our most Prominent and Influential People.

24. Always interline a Contract before signing it, merely to impress the Party of the First Part. The one who puts his Signature to Articles of Agreement drawn up by the Other Fellow is establishing a Dangerous Precedent.

25. Never pretend to have Money except when you are in Straits. The Poor Man who pretends to have a Bank Account betters his Credit and takes no Risk. But the Prosperous Individual who counts his Money in the Street, forthwith will be invited to attend a Charity Bazaar.

"Is that all?" asked the Young Fox, when he had concluded the reading.

"I thought that would be enough for one Dose," replied the Old Fox.

"But you have not put in anything about depositing a certain Sum in the Bank every Week," said Fox, Jr. "I had always supposed that was the inevitable No. 1 of Parental Suggestions."

"I omitted that time-honored Instruction because I hope you will keep your Money out of the Bank," said the Old Fox. "It is so easy to sign Checks. If you find a Surplus accumulating, go in for Life Insurance, and then you may reasonably hope for the allotted Threescore and Ten Years."

And the Young Fox took the Truth Tablets out to have them Framed.

Moral: *Even the Elders can give a number of Helpful Hints.*

The Fable of the Parlor Blacksmith who was Unable to put it Right Over the Plate

Once there was a left-handed Society Selling-Plater who never landed in the Money.

Of all the Sexes that roam the Earth his pick was the Feminine. He was very partial to the Women Folks. Even the Blondines who work the Tooth-Picks in the Rotunda, and the Fat Ones who talk Baby Talk, and the Chickadees who chew Gum on the Trolley, and the dark-eyed Duennas who forget to do up their Back Hair, and the Lumpy Ones who never go all the way around with the Powder Puff, and the Flitty Ones who give the Soubrette Zip when they turn the Corner, and the Mopey Ones who wear Wrappers and eat Pickles, and the little Maudie Freshes who turn out on Saturday Night looking for Drummers, and the Spinkly Ones in Rainy Day Skirts who lead Dogs, and a good many others who never get into the Christy Pictures—they may have had their Failings but they looked Purty Fair to him.

The last one out was always Number One with Philo, for such was the Name of Our Hero.

During many a long Afternoon when he should have been busy with the Books, Philo leaned back, combing his Mustaches with a Steel Pen and looking at the Wall. He could see himself in a Cozy Corner under a Red Light. Beside him sat a Prize Beaut of the kind that makes a Star Feature for the Sunday Paper. She was holding him by the Hand and whispering, "You for Me, and nothing else doing."

Almost every Nightfall he would change to a White Vest and start out to see if he couldn't make the Lithograph come true.

Philo always had his Plan of Campaign ribbed up. He knew what he was going to say when she came breezing into the Front Room. Then when she had said so-and-so as a playful Come-Back he would say something Keen, apparently right off the Reel, and that would lead up to the Scene in the Cozy Corner.

Philo was always Letter Perfect at Rehearsals, but when it came to the Night Show he was a Scamp.

The Trouble was that the Little Lady never came back with the Right Cue. After about two Moves she would hand him a Liner which he would Muff. Then for the next five Minutes he would be trying to rub the Varnish off the Chair, using himself for the Purpose.

Or perchance when he showed up with his Lassoo hidden under his Coat and his Soul steeled to Determination, he would find two or three other Beaux on the Premises, all organized to block him off. Some twenty Minutes later, Philo would be up stage reading a Magazine.

After being Frosted from Head to Foot, our Young Friend decided that one who would induce a Timid Girl to move over and be Chummy, must not go after her but compel her to follow the Trail. Philo read in a Book costing $1.18 at a Department Store that the blasé Man of the World who treated them with cold and smiling Indifference, simply got them all worked up.

The Game plays out as follows: Cynical Ike with the dark, piercing Eyes and the lines of a Great Sorrow marked on his Handsome Face tells Dora that all Women are alike. This Talk goes best with a Turkish Cigarette. Dora tells him that he is Off. She says that there are Women in the World capable of Steadfast Love. Ike springs a pensive Sigh and says Ah, if he could believe it. Thereupon it is up to her to prove it or lose the Argument, and that's the Answer.

So Philo went around telling every one who would listen to him that Women are fickle ever. When he called he sat as far down in the Chair as he could get and said cruel Things about the World of Fashion. He wanted to get away from all the vain Pretendings of Artificial Society. He would never Marry.

He worked this along the entire Chain of Boarding Houses and no one teased him to change his Mind. Some said that Philo had been given the Hooks and was Sore. In the Books, all the swell Lookers are supposed to get out and chase the

Woman-Hater, but up in the 5th Ward, where Philo resided, the Recipe was no good.

Accordingly he switched. The second Book that fell into his Hands pictured the Young Fellow who simply keeps at the Girl and snoops around and plays House Dog until her Woman's Heart is touched by his Slavish Devotion. Philo began to camp out at the Home of a Brunette. At the end of six days she shivered at the Sight of him. After he had been given the Headache Answer three times in one Week he pulled down his Entry Money and coppered the whole Scheme.

Once he attempted the Impetuous Line of Business. It always works out on the Stage. The Object is to nail the Girl without giving her a Chance to become acquainted and Investigate. First or second meeting and then Speech about having loved her for Years before seeing her—Arm around Waist before there is time to jump—Bing!

One Moonlit Evening it was that $12-a-week Philo with a Vocabulary of 82 Words started out to win the Fair One with just one passionate Whirlwind that would carry her off her Feet.

He moved alongside, got a Split Infinitive crossed with a defective Adverb and died on everything except the Hug. Inasmuch as she never stood for any Strong-Arm Plays until after the Fourth Call she decided that she had been Insulted. She said that her Father would kill him. He took a short cut across the Lawn and escaped into the Alley back of the Engine House. Fortunately she had other Callers that Evening and became so Interested that she forgot to speak to Father.

Philo began to weaken on the Systems. Yet he knew that there was some certain Way of going at it, for he could see what was being pulled off all around him. Every Night when he was out scanning the Hammocks and Front Porches in order to spot his Destiny, he saw Whole Bunches of them snuggled together in the Twilight. He wondered how they managed to Last.

As for him, the Girl Proposition had him down and out.

If he kept quiet, he was a Stick. If he talked against time, he made Breaks.

If he complimented other Girls, he lost his Number. If he toasted other Girls, he insulted her Dearest Friends.

If he tried to Coddle, she called for Help. If he didn't she would begin to Yawn at about 9.30.

He had tried all known Methods that are supposed to be Winners and he was still a thousand miles from Cozy Corner.

One day he struck upon the Explanation of the whole sad State of Affairs. He decided that he was a Shell-Fish.

Moral: *Never play a System.*

The Fable of the He-Flirt who was very Jimpsy in the Hotel Office but a Phoney Piece of Work when Turned Loose in a Flat

A Drove of Homeless Bachelors was herded every Night in a sad European Hotel. One of them was a Lady-Killer, who didn't deny it. He had left a Trail of Broken Hearts from Penobscot, Me., to Puget Sound. He had the Style of Beauty made familiar by the Wood-Cuts in the Weekly Story Paper. He was the Police Gazette's Idea of a Gent. Also he was an identical Ringer for the polished Villain of the Ten-Twent-and-Thirt Repertoire Troupe. He had a long, silky Gambler's Mustache and he wore embroidered Suspenders. He was Elegant in Every Detail. Trust him for that.

His name should have been Chilton Travers or Lionel Lyndhurst, but his Parents could not foretell that he would grow up to be Manicured once a Week, so they called him Bill.

He wore Satin Fronts and Velvet Collars and put Cologne on his Eye-Brows. Bill had massive Jewels on each hand and a Watch-Charm the size of a Padlock. When he had combed his Hair so that it stood up in front, à la the Polite Brakeman, and whitened himself with Talcum Powder, and splashed himself with Musk and eaten a few Cachous to perfume the Breath, he was more than Satisfied with himself. He wore sharp-toed Patent Leathers, with Green Tops, at all Hours of the Day and Night. Bill read the *Smart Set* every Month and told how much his Clothes cost, and before he had conversed with a Stranger very long he would bring up the Subject of Silk Underwear. One of the yearning Ambitions of his Life was to own a Seal-Skin Overcoat.

When Bill was on the Road there was never a Waitress with a Waspy Waist and high-heeled Shoes that did not tremble violently when she handed him his Tenderloin of Beef Larded with Mushrooms. It is not often that a poor Working Girl gets a Chance to see the real Kafoozalum, although she often reads about him in The Duchess.

At the Hotel which he illuminated with his Presence, Bill was wont to gather a few Friends about him and tell of all the Happy Homes he had wrecked. He let it be understood that when he held up one Finger and whistled, they came running from all Directions.

His Stock Narrative always began with a Scene in a Parlor Car. According to his Tell it was practically impossible for him to ride any Distance in a Pullman without having some Society Girl of ravishing Beauty fix a hungry Gaze on him and begin to wig-wag for a Better acquaintance. She was usually the Daughter of a Cincinnati Millionaire, with a Swell Place on Walnut Hill, or mayhap he learned afterward that she belonged to a Prominent Family living in Euclid Avenue, Cleveland. If he cared to mention Names he could tell of a certain Party that moved in the very highest Push of Fifth Avenue, who wanted to break off an Engagement with a Guy from Boston, and all on his Account. He was a Devil among the Women, and he admitted it. As soon as a Lady had counted up his Rings and Lockets and got a good whiff of the Musk, she was ready to play the White Slave. Sometimes, when the Pipe was drawing very freely, he would tell all about being invited out to spend the Evening with a certain Queen whose Father owned one of the principal Banks in Omaha. To prove that all he said was True, he would show a Pink Envelope with Sealing Wax on the back of it. Those who had obtained a Flash of these Missives noticed that they were addressed in Blue Ink, with a little Curly Tail to each Capital Letter, thus proving that they must have been written by Heiresses.

One Peculiar Fact in connection with the Killings made by this Commercial Don Juan was that all the Victims of his Fatal Beauty lived at least 200 miles away. Here in the Town which was Headquarters for him, he seemed comparatively Harmless. He could put on his fawn-colored Prince Albert with a Red Carnation and a jaundice-colored Cravat, and carry his gold-headed Cane all up and down the main Thoroughfares and then come back to the European Hotel without having any of the Elite tagging after him. In fact, if he hadn't Confessed so often, no one would have suspected that Rainbow Bill, the human Mardi Gras, had ever cut any Melons outside of the Switchmen's Ball.

At this same Hotel there lived two or three Young Fellows who did not use Cocoa Cream or Scented Soap, and not one of them had ever made Cruel Sport of the trusting Affections of a Railway President's only Child. They thought they were good and lucky if they could sally out after Nightfall and while away a careless Hour with a few nice Stenographers and Music Teachers. All they expected was a little 'Coon Stuff on the Piano and then some Dutch Lunch.

It happened that they told the Girls about Rainbow Bill who lived down at the Hotel and was receiving come-back-to-me Letters every Minute or two from the Leaders of Kansas City's 400 and the Prize Beauties of Lexington, Ky., to say nothing of the Hot-Looker whose Old Man had just built a $250,000 Hut outside of Philadelphia.

The Girls said they should like to meet one who had got in right with so many of the First Families, but they were afraid that he wouldn't pause to dally with them, seeing that they were on Salary. Perhaps one accustomed to show off in a spacious Drawing Room would find his Style more or less cramped when thrown into the 6x9 Parlor of a $22 Flat. However, the Boys said they would try to inveigle Rainbow Bill. Only, they gave Fair Warning that he claimed to be a Sorcerer and that after he looked a Soubrette in the Eye and made a couple of Passes, she was His, and took orders from no one else. The Girls said they were ready to take a Chance. Besides, they had been Vaccinated.

The Boy with the Wardrobe of many Colors did not show any Eagerness when told that he was wanted up at the Flat. He began to back water and fake up Excuses. They had to tell him that the Girls had seen him on the Street and were dying for an Introduction. At last he fixed himself up until he smelled like a box of Cashmere Bouquet, and they took him in Tow.

He began to lose from the Minute that he came up the front Steps. His Reputation had preceded him and it was the kind that would sink a Ship. The nifty tailor-made Damsel of Nineteen Hundred and Something doesn't ask any better Sport than to walk up and down on the tonsorial Wretch who fancies that he is Irresistible. As soon as a Man Bills himself as a Girl-Tamer, the whole Sorority wants to get out and stab him to death with Hat Pins. For some Reason, the latest variety of New Woman resents the Suggestion that she is a Soft Mark for the curbstone Masher who stands in front of Cigar Stores and Works the Banjo Eye.

It may have been True that Rainbow Bill cut a wide Swath in Kansas City and visited all the warm Tamales in St. Paul, but up in the dinky Flat he was one cold Portion of Lobster à la Newburgh. The Girls sparred him back into a Corner and kidded him to a Frazzle. They passed the Sarcastic Shots at the Rate of one per Second with no Return, although frequently he had told that he was a great Hand for Repartee. They hurled the Javelins into him until he curled like a Rubber Band. The fascinating Wiles that had played such Havoc among the Society Belles at other Points somehow refused to come to the Surface. All he could do was shift his Legs and look Sheepish. In the whole course of the Evening he found his Voice 8 times, but he didn't say anything that would have induced a Girl to leave her comfortable Home. After the first half hour they wouldn't have known he was there at all, if he hadn't got in the Way occasionally.

Moral: *Copper all Confessions.*

The Fable of the Reckless Wife who had no One to Watch Her

A young Couple sat and looked devouringly at each other for the first six months of the Life Sentence and finally it became rather trying on the Eyes. Therefore he was glad to be called away for a couple of Days. It was his first Vacation since leasing the Flat, and he sent word to some of his former Running Mates to meet him at the Train, as he could transact his Business in about 20 Minutes, after which he would remove his Bridle and begin to burn Holes in the Track.

They knew just what would appeal to a quiet Home Body, 400 miles from his own Fireside. They took him in Tow and gave him a Square Meal every Hour. Then they stood him under a Shower Bath and turned the whole Wine Card on him. He played Golf Pool until he was chalked all over and then he played Poker until he had to feel to see if the Ante was there. The Clerk at the Hotel saw him twice—once when he Registered and once when he came to get his Baggage. He fell into a Sleeper and told the Porter to make up Berths until ordered to stop. In the morning when he awoke with a Head of Seven Gables and reached for his Bromo, he realized that he had Enjoyed himself.

While he was away, working a combine of Business and Recreation, the Wife went on a regular Lark. She called in a former Chum and they sallied out in their Circus Gowns and ordered up Pine Apple Soda regardless and took in a Matinee where the Leading Man looked right at them occasionally and then they ate Marshmallows all the way Home. They put on Old Wrappers and cooked something in a Chafing-Dish, and the Wife brought out some of her Preserved Letters and read them and then they turned in together and giggled half the Night.

But, fortunately, the Husband never found out how she had carried on.

Moral: *The Reaction is something Terrible.*

The Fable of Lutie, the False Alarm, and How She Finished About the Time that She Started

Lutie was an Only Child. When Lutie was eighteen her Mother said they ought to do something with Lutie's Voice. The Neighbors thought so, too. Some recommended killing the Nerve. Others allowed that it ought to be Pulled.

But what Mamma meant was that Lutie ought to have it cultivated by a Professor. She suspected that Lutie had a Career awaiting her, and would travel with an Elocutionist some day and have her Picture on the Programme.

Lutie's Father did not warm up to the Suggestion. He was rather Near when it came to frivoling away the National Bank Lithographs. But pshaw! The Astute Reader knows what happens in a Family when Mother and the Only Child put their Heads together to whipsaw the Producer. One day they shouldered him into a Corner and extorted a Promise. Next Day Lutie started to Take.

She bought a red leather Cylinder marked "Music," so that people would not take it to be Lunch. Every morning about 9 o'clock she would wave the Housework to one side and tear for a Trolley. Her Lessons cost the Family about twenty cents a Minute. She took them in a large Building full of Vocal Studios. People who didn't

LUTIE

know used to stop in front of the Place and listen, and think it was a Surgical Institute.

There were enough Soprani in this one Plant to keep Maurice Grau stocked up for a Hundred Years. Every One thought she was the Particular One who would sooner or later send Melba back to Australia and drive Sembrich into the Continuous. Lutie was just about as Nifty as the Next One.

When she was at Home she would suck Lemons and complain about Draughts and tell why she didn't like the Other Girls' Voices. She began to act like a Prima Donna, and her Mother was encouraged a Lot. Lutie certainly had the Artistic Temperament bigger than a Church Debt.

Now before Lutie started in to do Things to her Voice

she occasionally Held Hands with a Young Man in the Insurance Business, named Oliver. This Young Man thought that Lutie was all the Merchandise, and she regarded him as Permanent Car-Fare.

But when Lutie began to hang out at the Studios she took up with the Musical Set that couldn't talk about anything but Technique and Shading and the Motif and the Vibrato. She began to fill up the Parlor with her new Friends, and the first thing Oliver knew he was in the Side Pocket and out of the Game.

In his own Line this Oliver was as neat and easy-running as a Red Buggy, but when you started him on the topic of Music he was about as light and speedy as a Steam Roller. Ordinarily he knew how to behave himself in a Flat, and with a good Feeder to work back at him he could talk about Shows and Foot-Ball Games and Things to Eat, but when any one tried to draw him out on the Classics, he was unable to Qualify. In short, he was a Crab.

When Lutie and her Musical Acquaintances told about Shopan and Batoven he would sit back so quiet that often he got numb below the Hips. He was afraid to move his Feet for fear some one would notice he was still in the Parlor and ask him how he liked Fugue No. 11, by Bock. He had never heard of any of these People, because they did not carry Tontine Policies with his Company.

Oliver saw that he would have to scratch the Musical Set or else begin to Read Up, so he changed his Route. He cancelled all Time with Lutie, and made other Bookings.

Lutie then selected for her Steady a Young Man with Hair who played the 'Cello. He was so wrapped up in his Art that he acted Dopey most of the time, and often forgot to send out the Laundry so as to get it back the same Week. Furthermore he didn't fly to the Suds any too often. He never saw more than $3 at one time; but when he snuggled up alongside of a 'Cello and began to tease the long, sad Notes out of it, you could tell that he had a Soul for Music. Lutie thought he was Great, but what Lutie's Father thought of him could never get past the Censor. Lutie's Father regarded the whole Musical Set as a Fuzzy Bunch. He began to think that in making any Outlay for Lutie's Vocal Training he had bought a Gold Brick. When he first consented to her taking Lessons his Belief had been that after she had practiced for about one Term she would be able to sit up to the Instrument along in the Dusk before the Lamps were lit, and sing, "When the Corn is Waving, Annie Dear," "One Sweetly Solemn Thought," or else "Juanita." These were the Songs linked in his Memory with some Purple Evenings of the Happy Long Ago. He knew they were Chestnuts, and had been called in, but they suited him, and he thought that inasmuch as he had put up the Wherewith for Lutie's Lessons he ought to have some kind of a Small Run for his Money.

Would Lutie sing such Trash? Not she. She was looking for Difficult Arias from the Italian, and she found many a one that was Difficult to sing, and probably a little more Difficult to Listen To.

The Voice began to be Erratic, also. When Father wanted to sit by the Student's Lamp and read his *Scribner's,* she would decide to hammer the Piano and do the whole Repertoire.

But when Mother had Callers and wanted Lutie to Show Off, then she would hang back and have to be Coaxed. If she didn't have a Sore Throat, then the Piano was out of Tune, or else she had left all of her Good Music at the Studio, or maybe she just couldn't Sing without some one to Accompany her. But after they had Pleaded hard enough, and everybody was Embarrassed and sorry they had come, she would approach the Piano timidly and sort of Trifle with it for awhile, and say they would have to make Allowances, and then she would Cut Loose and worry the whole Block. The Company would sit there, every one showing the Parlor Face and pretending to be entranced, and after she got through they would Come To and tell how Good she was.

She made so many of these Parlor Triumphs that there was no Holding her. She had herself Billed as a Nightingale. Often she went to Soirées and Club Entertainments, volunteering her Services, and nowhere did she meet a Well-Wisher who took her aside and told her she was a Shine—in fact, the Champion Pest.

No, Lutie never got out of her Dream until she made a bold Sashay with a Concert Company. It was her Professional Début.

Father fixed it. The Idea of any one paying Real Money to hear Lutie sing struck him as being almost Good enough to Print. But she wouldn't be Happy until she got it, and so she Got It right where the Newport Lady wears the Rope of Pearls.

On the First Night the mean old Critics, who didn't know her Father or Mother, and had never been entertained at the House, came and got in the Front Row, and defied Lutie to come on and Make Good. Next Morning they said that Lutie had Blow-Holes in her Voice; that she hit the Key only once during the Evening, and then fell off backward; that she was a Ham, and Her Dress didn't fit her, and she lacked Stage Presence. They expressed Surprise that she should be attempting to Sing when any bright Girl could learn to pound a Type-Writer in Four Weeks. They wanted to know who was responsible for her Appearance, and said it was a Shame to String these Jay Amateurs. Lutie read the Criticisms, and went into Nervous Collapse. Her Mother was all Wrought Up, and said somebody ought to go and kill the Editors. Father bore up grimly.

Before Lutie was Convalescent he had the Difficult Italian Arias carted out of the house. The 'Cello Player came to call one Day, and he was given Minutes to get out of the Ward.

By the time Oliver looked in again Lutie was more than ready to pay some Attention to him. She is now doing a few quiet Vocalizations for her Friends. When some one who hasn't Heard tells her she is good enough for Opera, they have to open the Windows and give her more Air.

Moral: *When in Doubt, try it on the Box-Office.*

What the College Incubator Did for One Modest Lambkin

One Autumn Afternoon a gray-haired Agriculturist took his youngest Olive Branch by the Hand and led him away to a Varsity. Wilbur was 18 and an Onion. He had outgrown his last year's Tunic, and his Smalls were hardly on speaking terms with his Uppers. He had large, warty Hands, which floated idly at his sides, and his Wrists resembled extra Sets of Knuckles. When he walked, his Legs gave way at the Hinge and he Interfered. On his Head was a little Wideawake with a Buckle at the Side. Mother had bobbed his Hair and rubbed in a little Goose-Grease to make it shine. The Collar that he wore was size 13, and called the Rollo Shape. It rose to a Height of a half-inch above his Neck-Band. For a Cravat he had a Piece of Watered Silk Ribbon with Butterflies on it.

Wilbur had his Money tied up in a Handkerchief, and he carried a Paper Telescope loaded down with one Complete Change and a Catalogue of the Institution showing that the Necessary Expenses were not more than $3.40 per Week.

As the Train pulled away from Pewee Junction Wilbur began to Leak. The Salt Tears trickled down through the Archipelago of Freckles. He wanted to Crawfish, but Paw bought him a Box of Crackerjack and told him that if he got an Education and improved his Opportunities some day he might be County Superintendent of Schools and get his $900 a Year just like finding it. So Wilbur spunked up and said he would try to stick it out. He got out the Catalogue and read all of the copper-riveted Rules for the Moral Guidance of Students.

The Curriculum had him scared. He saw that in the next four Years he would have to soak up practically all the Knowledge on the Market. But he was cheered to think that if he persevered and got through he would be entitled to wear an Alpaca Coat and a Lawn Tie and teach in the High-School, so he took Courage and began to notice the Scenery.

Wilbur was planted in a Boarding-House guaranteed to provide Wholesome Food and a Home Influence. Father went back after making a final Discourse on the importance of learning most everything in all of the Books.

Nine Months later they were down at the Depot to meet Wilbur. He had written several times, saying that he could not find time to come Home, as he was in pursuit of Knowledge every Minute of the Day, and if he left the Track, Knowledge might gain several Laps on him. It looked reasonable, too, for the future Superintendent of Schools had spent $400 for Books, $200 for Scientific Apparatus, and something like $60 for Chemicals to be used in the Laboratory.

When the Train suddenly checked itself, to avoid running past the Town, there came out of the Parlor Car something that looked like Fitz, on account of the Padding in the Shoulders. Just above one Ear he wore a dinky Cap about the size of a Postage Stamp. The Coat reached almost to the Hips and was buttoned below. The Trousers had enough material for a suit. They were reefed to show feverish Socks of a zigzag Pattern. The Shoes were very Bull-Doggy, and each had a wide Terrace running around it. Father held on to a Truck for Support. Never before had he seen a genuine Case of the inflammatory Rah-Rahs.

Wilbur was smoking a dizzy little Pipe from which the Smoke curled upward, losing itself in a copious Forelock that moved gently in the Breeze. Instead of a Collar, Wilbur was wearing a Turkish Towel. He had the Harvard Walk down pat. With both Hands in his Pockets, the one who had been pursuing Knowledge teetered towards the Author of his Being and said, "How are you, Governor?"

Father was always a Lightning Calculator, and as he stood there trying to grasp and comprehend and mentally close in, as it were, on the Burlap Suit and the Coon Shirt and the sassy Pipe, something told him that Wilbur would have to switch if he expected to be County Superintendent of Schools.

"Here are my Checks," said Wilbur, handing over the Brasses. "Have my Trunks, my Golf Clubs, my portable Punching-Bag, the Suit-Case and Hat-Boxes sent up to the House right away. Then drive me Home by the Outside Road, because I don't want to meet all these Yaps. They annoy me."

"You'd better git out of that Rig mighty quick if you don't want to be Joshed," said his Parent. "Folks around here won't stand for any such fool Regalia, and if you walk like a frozen-toed Hen you'll get some Hot Shots or I miss my Calkilations."

"Say, Popsy, I've been eating Raw Meat and drinking Blood at the Training-Table, and I'm on Edge," said Wilbur, expanding his Chest until it bulged out like a Thornton Squash. "If any of these local Georgie Glues try to shoot their Pink Conversation at me I'll toss them up into the Trees and let them hang there. I'm the Gazabe that Puts the Shot. Any one who can trim a Policeman and chuck a Hackman right back into his own Hack and drive off with him doesn't ask for any sweeter Tapioca than one of these Gaffer Greens. The Ploughboy who is muscle-bound and full of Pastry will have a Proud Chance any time that he struts across my Pathway. In my Trunks I have eight suits a little warmer than this one and 47 pairs of passionate Hose. I'm out here to give the Cornfields a Touch of High Life. It's about time that your Chaws had a Glimpse of the Great Outside World. Any one who gets Fussy about the Color-Combinations that I spring from

Day to Day will be chopped up and served for Lunch. To begin with, I'm going to teach you and Mother to play Golf. If these Mutts come and lean over the Fence and start to get off their Colored-Weekly Jokes we'll fan the Hillside with them."

"What do they teach up at your School—besides Murder?" inquired Father. "I thought you wanted to be County Superintendent of Schools."

"I've outgrown all those two-by-four Ambitions," was the Reply. "I'm going to be on the Eleven next Fall. What more could you ask?"

That very week Wilbur organized a Ball Team that walloped Hickory Crick, Sand Ridge, and Sozzinsville. He had the whole Township with him. Every Cub at Pewee Junction began to wear a Turkish Towel for a Collar and practise the Harvard Walk.

Moral: *A Boy never blossoms into his full Possibilities until he strikes an Atmosphere of Culture.*

The Subordinate Who saw a Great Light

Once there was an Employé who was getting the Nub End of the Deal. He kicked on the long Hours and the small Salary, and helped to organize a Clerks' Protective Association. He was for the Toiler as against the Main Squeeze.

In order to keep him simmered down, the Owners gave him an Interest. After that he began to perspire when he looked at the Pay-Roll, and it did seem to him that a lot of big, lazy Lummixes were standing around the Shop doing the Soldier Act. He learned to snap his Fingers every time the Office Boy giggled. As for the faithful old Book-Keeper who wanted an increase to $9 and a week's Vacation in the Summer, the best he got was a little Talk about Contentment being a Jewel.

The Associate Partner played Simon Legree, all except the make-up. The saddest moment of the Day for him was when the whole Bunch knocked off at 6 o'clock in the Evening. It seemed a Shame to call 10 Hours a Full Day. As for the Saturday Half-Holiday Movement, that was little better than Highway Robbery. Those who formerly slaved alongside of him in the Galleys had to address him as Mister, and he had them numbered the same as Convicts.

One Day an Underling ventured to remind the Slave-Driver that once he had been the Friend of the Salaried Minion.

"Right you are," said the Boss. "But when I plugged for the lowly Wage-Earner I never had been in the Directors' Office to see that beautiful Tableau entitled 'Virtue copping out the Annual Dividend.' I don't know that I can make the Situation clear to you, so I will merely remark that all those who get on our side of the Fence are enabled to catch a new Angle on this Salary Question."

Moral: *For Educational Purposes, every Employé should be taken into the Firm.*

Rugged Hiram and Hiram's Giddy Wife

Once there was a staid Business Man who was hooked up with a hoop-la Spender. It was often remarked that Hiram's Wife seemed to take it for granted that Treasury Notes grew on Trees. She wore those long, lozenge-shaped Rings that blind the Spectator, and she had a different Sunburst for every Day in the Week and a Diamond Tarara that made the other Women sizzle with Envy. She wore a trailing Work Gown that kept coming into the Room long after she had entered.

Now and then she would give a Party at which $80 worth

of Spinach would be hung on the Chandeliers. The highest-priced Caterer in Town would deal out the sparkling Conversation Water as if Brut and Buttermilk cost about the same.

She was, in very Sooth, among the highest of the Rollers, but Hiram stood for the Bills with nary a Whimper. He was proud to be the Husband of the Lady Ki-Bosh of the Local Knickerbockers.

He never pranced into the Ring himself for Fear that he might Interfere or throw a Shoe, but he sat back in Section A and rooted for the Missus. Every time she was awarded a Blue Ribbon for another Social Triumph, he was pleased beyond Compare.

Hiram was a Child of Nature, and he never had been able to outgrow his Birthright. Even when he was attired in his $135 Evening Clothes, one could tell by looking at him that he knew how to milk a Cow. He had more Hands and Feet than he could dispose of at one Time.

Hiram could not comb his Hair so that it would Stay, and although he had been in the City for 30 years he never contrived to get the Hang of a tie-it-yourself Bow Tie, so he used the kind that fastens behind with a little Buckle. It was even said that Hiram was unable to put the Studs in his Shirt without getting Finger-Marks on the Bosom. Hiram's Wife or daughter Jessie always had to go to his Room and look him over and turn him around a couple of times before they dared to lead him out where the Company could see him.

When there was a Theatre-Party, Hiram always sat back between the Curtains so as to avoid spoiling the Picture, and at the same time keep the Draught away from the other People. At a Dinner-Party he was usually put in between two gabby Girls who had tacit Instructions to keep him elbowed into the Background.

And yet, withal, Hiram was a Man of Sterling Worth and many admirable Qualities. He was the Family Gibraltar, while his Wife and Jessie were supposed to be mere Floral Ornaments. Best of all, Hiram was known to be a Star at getting the Coin. The Fact that the Family put up such a tall Front in the Society Column helped the Public to believe that Hiram was as good as Old Wheat and as prosperous as a Kansas Farmer. And he was supposed to be long on Business Integrity. It was argued that one so Yappy would have to be correspondingly Honest.

Hiram was so Severe and Puritanical and had so much clinging Agricultural Simplicity that no one dreamed the Truth about him. In Reality, his Arteries were surcharged with Sporting Blood. When no one suspected it, he liked to put on a Mask and sneak out and hold up the Stock Market. That is what he did until one sad Day in May the Stock Market up and Did him. He got it right where the Hired Girl wears the Ruching.

Hiram came home as Pale as a Ghost and broke the News that he was in the Hole. He hesitated to tell the Wife, for she was a Fragile Being, unaccustomed to the rude Buffets of the Strenuous Life, and he feared that such a cruel Blow might crush her. But he finally divulged the frightful Truth and then flopped to the Settee and began to Bluff about killing himself, so that she could get the Insurance Money. She told him to Behave, and then she went out and made a Cup of Strong Tea for him.

Hiram had been an Imposing Figure so long as he had his Financial Underpinning, but when they yanked away his Supports he did a horrible Collapse. When he got the Swing in the Plexus and toppled over he proved to be a sorry Quitter. He lay on his Back and claimed a Foul, while his Wife and Jessie hustled around to save some of the Wreckage.

They gave up the Servants and soaked the Jewels and moved into a smaller House. It was a rapid Come-Down, but even while they were doing the Parachute they continued to look Pleasant and be Game. Although their

Female Friends came around to express Sympathy and stick Pins in them, they forced the Angelic Smile and did not act a bit like Heavy Losers.

They had to take in Roomers and give Lessons in China-Painting in order to save Hiram from the Poor-House, and yet with all their Skimping and Economizing they never pretended to know Poverty.

When a Man loses his Money he goes to his Bedroom to drink himself into a Trance. A Woman lights the House from Cellar to Garret and sends out Invitations for a Party.

On an Income of about $3 a Week, Hiram's Wife and Daughter managed to keep up Appearances and occasionally have some of their Old Friends to Dinner. Hiram never understood how they managed it. When he looked at his empty Bank-Book and then out at the Cold World he was for giving up and disappearing beneath the Waves. His Wife braced him and told him to think of Jessie. Hiram wept and said there was no Hope for the Child of a Pauper. Notwithstanding which, Hiram's Wife kept the Family right along in the Swim and married Jessie to a desirable Catch. It is true that she starved the Household for six months in order to give the Young Couple a daisy Send-Off.

And all this time Hiram, the astute Business Manager, was standing around on one Foot like a Town Simpleton at a Kissing-Bee.

Hiram had learned how to do Things with Money, but he had to turn to his frivolous Wifey to find out how to Manage it when there was no Money.

In other words, Hiram discovered that Cash had been the Essence of his Existence while it had been the mere accidental Adjunct to his Wife's Social Campaigns.

Without a big Reserve he was a Smoke. She, minus her Check-Book, rose to greater heights of Diplomacy. In time she succeeded in resuscitating her groggy Husband and putting him back on the Track, but he had lost his Ginger. He was stoop-shouldered and gray as a Bat.

She turned up at the Club Meetings just as chipper as of Yore, only she came by Trolley instead of Coupé.

Moral: *It is the upheaval of Tough Luck that causes a Transfer of the Family Sceptre.*

The Galley Slave Who Was Just About To but Never Did

Once there was a Youth who tackled the Mercantile Career at a very light Stipend.

His chief Ambition in Life was to get so far ahead of the Game that he could afford a nice Cutaway Suit, a swell Derby for Sunday, and a 14-karat De Beers set in a massive Gold Band.

He learned to embrace the Country Trade and talk 175 Words per Minute, so that in a little while he had an Offer from an Opposition Concern. Whereupon he said he hated to leave, but—and the House stood for an Increase.

He came into the Cutaway and the Ring, and then he found that he needed a Spike-Tail and a Folding-Hat and a Cape-Coat. His Glad Raiment carried him right into Sussiety, and he began to meet Gazelles that suited him, so he figured on the Probable Expense of Keeping House.

He thought that if he could annex a good-looking Tottie with large, soulful Eyes, and take an Apartment and keep a Girl, then he would be fixed for sure.

So he went out for more Salary and carried the Bank-Book next to his Heart. At last the Proud Day arrived when he had his own Flat, with a rented Piano in the Front Room and Tidies on the Chairs. Before the Lease expired Pet discovered that the Dining-Room was too small, and began to dream Dreams of a House of their Own in which they could Entertain. So he tucked back his Cuffs and took a fresh Grip on the World of Trade, and boned like a Turk, making Payments on the House. He was beginning to look round-shouldered, but he drank plenty of Coffee and smoked fat Cigars and buckled down.

He had it all planned to take a good Rest as soon as he had lifted the Mortgage. He went so far as to send out for Time-Tables and look at the Pictures of People sitting around in Steamer Chairs enjoying the Sea Air.

He would have taken a nice, long Vacation, only he saw a Chance to break into the Firm. Accordingly he went in Debt up to his Eyes. He would lie awake at Night casting up his Liabilities and computing Interest. He talked to himself on the Street, and acted just the least bit Dippy. But he was determined to swing the Deal, and then, as soon as he was out of the Woods, he could take a Trip and hang around Picture-Galleries and ride in Gondolas and have the Time of his Life, with nothing to worry him.

For Years he had said that it was a Crime for any one Man to pile up more than $100,000. As soon as he went above that Figure it was a Case of sitting up Nights to count it. As soon as he had that Hundred Thousand raked up and tied in Bundles, then for a Quiet Spot near a Body of Water and a Naphtha Launch and the free, open Life of the Golf Links.

To the 50-cent Table-d'Hôte Fellow, 100,000 Samoleons in one Lump looks bigger than the Union Station, but the Man who is being gnawed by the Mazuma Bacillus thinks he is a Pauper unless he can count up Seven Figures. He is always sizing up alongside of Rockefeller and Morgan, and he feels like a Piker sitting in a stiff Poker Game with one White Seed.

Just about the time the Business Man counted up $100,000 to the Good he discovered that he needed seven Servants around the House. And the Missus could float downtown on a sunny Afternoon and make $1000 look like a Pinch of Small Change.

He set his Mark at One Million. Then, when he had that, out to the Sylvan Dell. He was going to be a Gentleman Farmer.

Every Office Building on Earth is congested with hollow-eyed Prisoners who are planning to be Gentleman Farmers. About next Year or Year after—away from the Hurly Burly and nothing to do except raise Chickens.

All of them have those Chicken Dreams. This Business Man whom we are describing even went so far as to pick out the kind of Chickens he was going to raise—Plymouth Rocks. He figured how many Eggs he could get per Hen, and sometimes, when the Pencil was working well, he estimated that he could make the Place self-supporting.

In the mean time he was humping himself and eating Pepsin Tablets and taking a little something every Night to make him Sleep.

The Business had developed so that he had fourteen Push-Buttons in front of him, and kept two Stenographers busy, and was jumping from the Long-Distance Phone to the Private Office most of the Time, and chewing up 30-cent Cigars, and in other Ways giving a correct Imitation of a Man who has a large and ambitious Family on Hand.

He began to look Wild out of the Eyes and had a severe Case of the Jumps, but he had to postpone that Rest for a little While, because no one else understood all the Details of the Business.

When the Doctor hinted about Nervous Prostration he said that he was trying to get the whole Organization down to a System, so that some one else could step in and run it, after which he expected to take a Place in the Country and raise Chickens. He told the Chicken Story so often he began to believe it himself.

In order to systematize the Large Business so that he could turn it over to some one else and then have his Vacation, he began to put in 16 hours a Day, and landed in the large Corner Room, with a Trained Nurse putting Ice on his Head and telling him he would be all right in a Day or so.

He had a Ticker put in at one side of the Bed, and

kept a Stenographer on hand up to the Afternoon that he departed this life.

It is said that when he went to his Reward he was met by a Celestial Attendant, who proved to be the Recording Angel.

"If you're the Recording Angel, get out your Book," said the Business Man. "I want you to take a few Letters for me."

Moral: *The Chicken Ranch is always in the Future Tense.*

The Ninety-Pound Knight-Errant and His Lady Fair

Once there was an Estimable Lady named Mrs. Killjoy who used to hunt for Trouble with a Search-Warrant.

She was not happy unless she was being Insulted. Before any one chirped she knew that she was going to have Bricks thrown at her Character.

Mrs. Killjoy held to the obsolete Theory that Man was put into this Mundane Trouble Factory to protect weak and defenceless Woman from all Slurs, Slights, and Insults. That is why she picked out for her True Knight an undeveloped Specimen, about the size of a Philadelphia Squab, with four-inch Biceps.

His steady Assignment was to fight her Battles. Mrs. Killjoy was one those Sensitive Plants who could not get into a Trolley without having some one rudely Stare at her. She always suspected that the He-Salesmen in the Stores were trying to make Love to her, and if any Man happened to be walking behind her on the same side of the Street she knew that she was being Pursued.

"Are you going to sit here and allow your Wife to be Insulted?"

That was the Speech she would hand him when they were out together. Then it was up to him to call some 200-pounder or else be prepared to lie awake half the Night and listen to the Story of her Wrongs.

Sometimes he suspected that she wanted to realize on his Life Insurance.

His usual Play was to promise to be an Avenger. Then he would hunt up the Person who had grossly insulted Mrs. Killjoy and apologize in her behalf and say that she was a trifle Dippy.

What Mrs. Killjoy needed was a Husband in a full Suit of Armor mounted on a White Horse and thirsting for Blood. She had read the wrong kind of Books. Husband knew that she would stack him up against it sooner or later.

Sure enough, one Day he found her in Tears and learned that the Man delivering the Coal had been Impertinent and had failed to remove his Hat while speaking to her. She wanted to know if Mr. Killjoy was a Man or a Mouse, and that settled it. He went out to roast the Teamster and she followed along to Gloat.

The Teamster was a Low-Brow with a 48-inch Chest, and he did not know a thing about the Henry of Navarre Business. He grabbed Mr. Killjoy and dusted the Bin with him.

While the Sufferer was in the Hospital waiting for the Bones to join, Mrs. Killjoy sat beside him and said, "As soon as you are well enough to be around you must hunt him up and shoot him."

"I will," said the brave Knight, "if I can get one of those Sandy Hook Guns that will carry six Miles."

Moral: *In these Days, Chivalry must wear a Tag or it will not be Recognized.*

SHORT STORIES

Preface to the Original Edition (1903)

These little stories and sketches have been rewritten from certain daily contributions to the Chicago *Record,* now the Chicago *Record-Herald.* They have been assembled into this little volume in the faint hope that they may serve as an antidote for the slang which has been administered to the public in such frequent doses of late. They are supposed to deal, more or less truthfully, with every-day life in Chicago.

THE AUTHOR.
(from *In Babel*)

"Buck" and Gertie

Buchanan Caster, or "Buck" (he preferred the latter title), was man of all work for a family on the boulevard. This family had come into wealth, and was making a weak effort to change its mode of life, without having any heart in the endeavor. "Buck" was the only man-servant and there was nothing of the servant in him. He was an independent product of a small town in Michigan, and, although he consented to curry the Chamberlain horses, mow the Chamberlain lawn, and even wear a tall hat while driving the Chamberlain carriage, he did so with the full mental reservation that he was "just as good" as any of the Chamberlains, living or dead, and possibly a few degrees keener on ordinary topics.

He assumed an easy familiarity with Jonas Chamberlain, the head of the family, and he addressed Harry Chamberlain, the son, by his first name. He respected Mrs. Chamberlain as a woman of sound judgment, but he considered it his privilege to disagree with her at times and enter into argument. He liked the two Chamberlain girls, and was willing to do almost any kind of favor for them, if properly approached.

"Buck" Caster considered that he was the one level-headed and responsible person around the Chamberlain premises. He was willing to receive suggestions from the Chamberlains, but he much preferred that they should come to him for advice. Usually they came.

The imported menials—those who sit in wooden stiffness on the carriage-boxes, who never relax their solemn features except to say, "Yes, mum," and who always see between themselves and their employers a vast and unbridgeable chasm—would have said that "Buck" was a total failure as a servant. Probably this was true. He never regarded himself as a servant. "Buck" seemed to feel that he was general manager for the Chamberlains.

He might have grown gray as superintendent of the family if it had not been for Gertrude.

She was the cook.

From the day of her arrival, when "Buck" carried the fragile yellow trunk up to the room under the roof, a change came over the household. "Buck's" whole conduct was altered. Much of his imperial dignity deserted him. He lost that air of bustling importance which made him the wonder of the small boys in the neighborhood.

He lacked industry, and when he drove the carriage he sat humped over and allowed the lines to hang loosely, so that as a driver he was a pitiable spectacle. A hired hand going to town with a load of oats would have made just as smart a picture.

The truth was, and it could not be concealed, that "Buck" was in love with Gertrude, the cook. He had been smitten severely and instantaneously.

She was a tall and cleanly creature of twenty-eight, a plodding worker, and a jewel for any household. At first she was pleased by "Buck's" kindly attentions, but when he began to show a desire to be assistant cook instead of general manager; when he lingered around the kitchen at unreasonable hours and stared at her devouringly, and especially when he began to send presents, she was deeply frightened.

Gertrude came from a conservative family in Will County, and she did not choose to approach matrimony in a gallop. Accordingly she repulsed "Buck" one night when he attempted to read to her a love-poem clipped from the Fireside Companion. She repulsed him, and she ordered him from the kitchen.

"Buck" went out that evening in company with an Irish coachman from the opposite side of the boulevard and drank beer in order to extinguish the devouring flames of his unrequited love.

Coming home at 10.30, and finding Gertrude still up, he denounced her in a voice that could be heard four lots away.

This was too much for the patient Chamberlains. Next day Jonas Chamberlain attempted to reprimand "Buck," who resented the interference with his inalienable and Michigan-fostered rights, and went away, leaving the family to shift for itself.

Gertrude was melancholy after that.

She seemed to hold herself accountable for his downfall and the breaking of the time-hallowed tie.

It may have been that when Gertrude drove "Buck" from the kitchen she did not intend the dismissal to be final. Certainly she was no happier, for "Buck's" successor, a mild German youth, could go to the kitchen a dozen times without so much as seeing her.

Gertrude became more melancholy, more pious, more regretful. She was a regular attendant at religious services. The family supposed that she attended the Methodist Church. Not so. She had taken up with the Salvation Army.

She had enlisted and was into the fight, consecrated and red-striped, before the family had a chance to remonstrate. She gave up her position, made a fervent little speech to Mrs. Chamberlain and then went away, burning with zeal.

Mrs. Chamberlain had been a friend to the army, but that day, as she drove to the intelligence office, she said several spiteful things about the abduction of cooks.

The Chamberlains heard nothing from either Buchanan or Gertrude, although many weeks passed by.

There came a Saturday night in the last month of the political campaign. A deafening band, followed by a straggle of shouters, had passed by. Two corner orators, drunken and incoherent, were shouting and sputtering at each other, while a crowd stood around and encouraged them by good-natured yelping. Above all the noise and confusion of partisan politics rose the swinging notes of an old-fashioned hymn, the thump of a drum, and the rattle of tambourines.

Harry Chamberlain had tired of the political shouters. He strolled off into the side street, where the swinging flame of a big torch lighted the circle of spectators drawn around a group of Salvation Army soldiers.

The singing had ceased, and a woman, mounted on a chair, was exhorting. Her high sonorous voice ran freely. She spoke with hysterical fervor, never hesitating, never in doubt as to what she wished to say. Harry Chamberlain idled along the edge of the crowd until he could see the face half-shaded by the poke-bonnet.

It was Gertrude.

Gertrude, the silent woman of the kitchen, transformed by religious ecstasy into a fiery advocate. He pressed forward and a second surprise awaited him.

There, in red shirt, with huge bass-drum strapped to him, his face illumined with interest in the speaker, rolling "Amens," fondling the drumstick with hot impatience, was Buchanan Caster.

Harry moved around so as to get near the drummer. Presently the meeting was over.

"Buck!" said Harry.

"Hello, Harry!" exclaimed the drummer. "Did you hear the sergeant speak? Ain't she wonderful? Say, I went into the meeting one night and saw her there. I went right up and joined. Then she knew I meant business. We're doin' a wonderful work— wonderful!"

"Take me back to the spot
Where I first saw the light."

The whole squad took up the song.

"Bang!" went the drum. Harry ran to get out of the way of the marchers.

He saw Gertrude lead on, swinging a tambourine above her head, and behind her was "Buck," leaning back until he could look straight up at the stars, and pounding the drum until it quivered.

Opening of Navigation

Two lake-faring men went hard at it with scrubs to clean the wooden effigy of Ceres, perched above the wheel-house of the Dudley Brown.

Ceres sat in a very stuff and conventional attitude, gazing directly up stream. She had a black spot painted in each eye, and the effect was to give her the appearance of staring with fascinated interest.

Could Ceres have seen from out those wooden eyes she would have learned that the big warehouses were dozing in warm sunshine. Along the docks which skirted them ran a most uneasy movement of men. Painters, in white suits, were suspended, like spiders, along the sides of the gaunt iron propellers and were covering the stains and rust of a winter's harbouring. Decks were being scrubbed down and rigging set taut and serviceable. In fact, Ceres would have known that the season was arousing itself.

Ceres wore a loose garment of fiery red. Her arms and face were white and rather scaly from repeated applications of white-lead. The sheaf which she carried in her left arm was done in brilliant yellow, and altogether she was a startling figure as she sat triumphant above the wheel-house, where the crowds passing on the bridge might look up and admire.

Ceres held this place of distinction because the Dudley Brown was a grain-carrying steamer plying between Chicago and Buffalo, and Ceres is the goddess of corn and tillage. The mariner could not pay a prettier compliment to the husbandman. Such courtesy was all the more graceful because one does not find many allusions to mythology along the Chicago river.

The two men who had climbed to the tin room of the wheel-house to cleanse the goddess were sailors—not the Jack Tars of youthful imagination, but sailors who had been reduced to deck-hands through the changes in navigation and the gradual supremacy of steam.

Dan Griswold had been a real Captain Marryat sailor once

upon a time, and had all the tattoo marks to prove it. He could splice and knot and reef, and he knew the names of all the sails and sheets, but this knowledge counted for nothing on the Dudley Brown. In the opinion of Dan Griswold it was not a vessel at all—just a huge grain-bin crowded along by a screw.

The sailor having lost his station, the pride and the clothes had gone with it. These two men scrubbing at the goddess were in blue flannel shirts and a cheap quality of factory-made farmer clothes. Dan Griswold wore a crumpled cap, and the younger man had a derby hat, bleached by the sun.

The younger man's name was Larry Pearson.

"I think she's clean, Larry," said Dan, passing the bucket and brush back to his companion and lowering himself, with a few grunts and sighs, from the roof of the wheel-house.

"She looks all right," said Larry.

"We've got to keep her looking all right," remarked Dan, as he picked up his bucket and walked aft. "She's the only woman we'll have aboard—and it's a good thing she can't hear what's bein' said."

Three men were perched along the rail on the sunny side of the boat warming their backs. One of them, Tony Baldwin, was reading aloud from a newspaper.

He stopped reading as Dan came up and said, "Here, Dan, you want to hear this."

"What is it?"

"They say the ice is out o' the straits, and they can get through now without a scratch. As soon as they can get insurance everything'll start. It's goin' to be the earliest season we've had for years."

"I'll be glad o' that," growled Larry, who had followed along. "It can't open any too soon for me."

"If I was on a real boat I wouldn't care, either," said Dan. "I'm forgettin' what a sail looks like, and I never did like the smell o' rain-water. That's all that thing is"—with a wave of the hand toward the lake—"a big puddle o' rain-water."

"I know why Dan ain't so anxious to get away this spring,"

said Tony, with a wink at the others. "He's stuck on the missus. Why don't you marry her, Dan, and settle down?"

"This ain't no time or place to talk about a lady," said Dan. "Leastways, not for low roustabouts to talk about her."

"Who's a low roustabout?" asked Tony, as he straightened his legs and came down to the deck. "Who's a low roustabout?"

"Well, who *is* a low roustabout if you ain't?"

"I'm goin' to make you swaller that."

"Come and do it."

They closed in, pawing at each other. They grappled and did a slow, heaving waltz together, and then went to the deck with Dan on top.

They were holding on, tugging and making inarticulate noises when the mate came. He was a very young man with a straw-coloured moustache.

"Here! Let go! Get up and out of here," he commanded, prodding the man underneath with his foot.

Dan untangled himself and came to his feet. He was breathing heavily and one eye had a bruised and watery appearance. Tony had been defeated by the rules of battle, but he bore no marks and was anxious to resume the fight.

"Go on—get off the boat, both of you," said the mate. "I don't want you around," and he gave his opinion of the two in language which may be imagined but cannot be quoted.

Dan jumped to the dock and went along the plank-driveway between the cold-storage warehouse and a freight-depot. One whole side of his face burned as if it had been chafed with a piece of sail-cloth. He wondered if the eye would show any colour. If so, he did not want to go to Mrs. Gunderson's, for he had told Mrs. Gunderson that he was not a fighting man. She would not have fighting or drinking men in the house, and that is why the discriminating captains and mates had come to board with her.

Dan had lived at the house for two winters, and during the second winter, because he could not be idle and because Mrs. Gunderson came to have a growing confidence in him, he was a sort of business manager for the establishment. He brought in reliable customers, kept track of the accounts, did much of the purchasing, and advised Mrs. Gunderson in all emergencies. For the first time in his wandering career he had found a taste of real domestic life, for one can never know domestic life unless one feels a proprietary interest.

Dan had outlived the sailors' period of romance. He had tired of the life on the grain steamers, but he had never dreamed that he could make a living or be useful in any way except on board a vessel. Here he was, preparing to begin another season of drudgery on the lakes, but he hated the prospect as he had never hated it before, and he began to realize that there was more of dignity and comfort in managing a three-decked boarding-house than in being ordered about as a common sailor. It was out of the bitterness of his daily reflections that he had resented Tony's playful remark.

Mrs. Gunderson met him as he entered the doorway.

"There you are, Mr. Griswold!" she exclaimed. "I've been lookin' for you. Mr. Cleary wants his bill. Lord bless us, Man! What's the matter with your eye?"

It may be remarked that although Mrs. Gunderson's husband (lost with a lumber schooner) had been a Norwegian, she was distinctly Scotch and Irish.

"I got into trouble with a fellow on the boat. It's all right. I'll make out Cleary's bill."

He went into his own room to work at the "books," and presently Mrs. Gunderson came in with a piece of steak for his eye, which he refused with gentle scorn.

"Mr. Cleary says the straits are open," remarked Mrs. Gunderson, as she admired Dan's work with the figures.

"Yes, they'll be gettin' away most any day now."

"Goodness only knows what we'll do when you're gone, Mr. Griswold. I've come to depend on you so much—with twenty men in the house."

"I hate to go myself, Mrs, Gunderson."

"Why can't you stay? I can pay you a little something,

or annyway your board—which you've been wantin' to pay. I need a man—I do that."

"So the boys on the boat say."

"They do?"

"Yes; I had my fight with a fellow that asked me why didn't I marry you."

"Bless you, the two girls have been askin' that for a month."

"Cleary owes you eleven fifty," said Dan, handing the bill to her. As she received it, she gave him a glance which he seemed to understand.

It was three days later that the mate of the Dudley Brown met Dan on the State Street bridge. Dan was smoking a cigar and surveying the river with the air of one who owned the stream and all abutting property.

"Look here, Dan, why haven't you been around?" he demanded. "I wouldn't be surprised if navigation opens by Saturday."

"Navigation can open and be damned," replied Dan. "I've quit the water."

The Barclay Lawn Party

The Barclays never went to summer-gardens where malt drink is served. They remained at home and looked at the factories. The Barclay home was a red-brick cube with a high and mournful roof. For ten years it had braced itself against the onsweeping rush of big machine-shops and steam-bakeries. Now it stood alone, a remnant of the old guard of that once sylvan street, surrounded and doomed, but not yet surrendering.

The Barclay girls were ready to move into a new house on the boulevard, but Mr. Barclay preferred to remain at home. The Methodist church was only three blocks to the west. Such friends as they cared to meet could still find the house. Here they had elbow room, green trees and flower-beds.

Sometimes, when the smoke drifted obligingly, the sunshine reached them—and it was "home."

One summer day the Barclay girls decided to live down the unfashionableness of the street by giving a lawn party.

The guests were to assemble at 6.30, and there was to be croquet playing in the area back of the grape-arbor. After that, when it came time for lighting the Chinese lanterns in the front yard, the company was to be seated at the small tables and provided with ice-cream, lemonade and cake. Two artists were to dispense mandolin music. After the serving of the refreshments and in the intervals between the mandolin selections, Eunice Barclay was to play a violin solo and the minister was to give some of the dialect recitations for which he had become justly famous with the members of his congregation. The minister had a fetching dialect, which was neither Yankee, German, nor Irish, but which he could fasten interchangeably on any kind of a character. Sometimes the minister would insert a dialect story into a sermon, and cause even Mr. Barclay to relax into an unwilling smile.

The lawn party started cheerfully. As the invited ones came straying in, Mrs. Barclay received them at the front porch and directed them to the croquet game back of the grape-arbor. There were but four players in the game, the other people sitting at the boundaries and simulating a sportive interest. Flora and the minister were partners against Mrs. Jennings and Mr. Talbot, who was the basso of the church-choir.

Flora convulsed the company when she exclaimed: "Oh, Mr. Talbot, I kissed you."

Now, what Flora really meant was that her croquet ball had kissed the croquet ball belonging to Mr. Talbot, but the startling wickedness implied in what she had said served to pleasantly horrify one and all. Afterward some of the women paled and pulled themselves back and seemed to feel that they had gone too far in their laughter, but they were reassured to observe that the minister was smiling and unruffled.

The Barclay girls did not vibrate with the full triumph of

their plans until the guests moved in a loose swarm to where the chairs and tables waited under the soft glow of lanterns. The mandolin orchestra, consisting of a mandolin and guitar, began to tinkle in the shadow of the porch.

It was still early dusk as the company gaily took possession of the small tables. The reserve which had chilled the beginning of the croquet contest had gradually worn away, and bright conversational flings went from table to table, many of them aimed at the minister, who was accused of inordinate haste in getting at the ice-cream. He laid the blame on Sister Crandall, and said she had asked him to lead the way to the refreshments. Mrs. Crandall protested in mock anger, and Mr. Barclay laughed immoderately, for he did not object to mischievous persiflage, under certain limitations.

A small boy had hung his face in a restful way between two pickets of the front fence and was gaping at the company. He was a big-eyed boy, and those who glanced toward him were made to think of a bloodless head impaled on two pikes. His silent scrutiny seemed to embarrass even the minister. Eunice Barclay went over to him and said, "Run away now, that's a good little boy." He backed away a few steps, staring at her sullenly, and when she rejoined the minister, he eased his chin between the pickets once more and grinned defiantly.

The orchestra began a medley of popular songs. Three other boys came to the fence and asked the big-eyed boy what was up. In a loud tone he urged them to keep still and listen to the music. Two men in their shirt-sleeves came along and stopped for the free concert. A little girl, having peeped through to get material for a connected story, ran away to arouse her friends and bring them to the scene of festival.

By the time the orchestra came to a rousing finish there were nine male persons punctuated along the fence, and a moment later no less than seven little girls mobilised and wriggled their fingers between the palings and began to point out objects of interest.

The Barclay guests stiffened themselves in their chairs and conversed laboriously, determined to ignore, and thus repel, the low curiosity.

But when one of the men in shirt-sleeves suggested to the orchestra that it "Play something else," a perceptible shiver ran through the assemblage. The little girls began to speculate earnestly as to the quality of the ice-cream.

Flora Barclay fanned herself rapidly and said, "Well, I never!" several times. Then she asked, "Don't you suppose they would go away if you asked them to, Mr. Talbot?"

Mr. Talbot weighs 130 pounds, and it may be that he was not meant for the commander's purple. But he said he would try.

He approached the fence, and, addressing the line of outsiders, said: "This is just a little private party, you know, and we'd be much obliged if you wouldn't stand here."

"We ain't hurtin' you," said one of the bulky men. "Go on with your show."

"I know, but the ladies who live here would rather that you —that is, wouldn't congregate here."

The men looked at one another, undecided, and then one of them said: "I don't like to be drove away from a place while I'm behavin' like a gentleman."

"That's right," mumbled his neighbour, his manner indicating that he had been stung in his American pride.

Mr. Talbot rejoined Flora and said he believed the men would go away presently. But they did not go away.

The orchestra played again, and the attendance increased. A crowd gathers itself like a rolling snowball. The larger it becomes, the greater is its drawing power.

Those who arrived during the second music loudly asked what was happening, and some of them seemed to believe that the music and the display of lanterns had a political significance. By this time the minister was comforting the women by telling them that it was "most unfortunate." Mr. Talbot was worried. Again Flora had asked him to "do something." What could he do?

Great was his relief when he saw an officer of the law. The policeman had parted a way for himself and was leaning heavily on the fence, a thoughtful expression mantling his face as he listened to the music.

"Please, Mr. Officer," said Mr. Talbot, "won't you get these people to go away? This is a private lawn party."

"Do they bother you?" asked the policeman.

"I should say so."

"I don't know as I've got any right to move 'em."

"Haven't got any right! Of course you've got a right. I appeal to you, sir. What's your number?"

"Oh, well, I'll try to get 'em back," said the policeman.

So he started along the fence, saying: "Come now, you'll have to move away from here." Every one retired before the majesty of his presence until he came to the man who previously had said that he didn't "want to be drove away." This man began to ask questions of the policeman.

"Who owns this sidewalk?" he demanded. "These people here don't own the street, do they? You don't have to do what they say, do you? Ain't I a tax-payer? Have I violated any ordinance, huh?"

The policeman was not a bureau of information. He took the inquisitive man by the neck and attempted to throttle him. The next moment there was a whirlwind battle.

The timid women under the Barclay trees screamed and caught hold of one another. The tables were upset and dishes went avalanching. Beyond the fence, a rosewood club twirled in the uncertain light and the tax-payer lunged to avoid it.

Then a patrol-wagon at the corner and two hundred spectators helping to load the damaged taxpayer into it.

Solemn, churchly men leading shaky women out of the Barclay front gate.

Flora in a summer-chair on the vine-sheltered porch, squirming with hysteria and Mr. Talbot trying to console her.

"Oh! Oh! The barbarians!" she gasped, with her handkerchief crumpled against her cheek.

"They are. They are, indeed," assented Mr. Talbot, reaching for her hand.

"We've wanted to move out of this dreadful neighborhood for years, but father—Oh—" and once more collapse seemed imminent. But Mr. Talbot was holding her hand in both of his hands.

"Let your father stay if he wants to, but you and me can go live wherever you say."

Ungrammatical and undiplomatic, true, but it served the purpose and it had to happen some time.

Best of the Farleys

John Farley has worked hard, taken the cheerful view of life, smoked a large amount of tobacco, "got drunk" occasionally and saved enough money to pay for a little house in Pitkin Street. He stands well with the foreman and is a favorite at the corner bar, for he is a wit and a commentator. He is prosperous, according to the division of wealth in Pitkin Street—prosperous and proud. His pride is Rosie.

She was born at the Pitkin Street house, and in her childhood she ranged through the alleys and lumber by-ways that led to the river. Mrs. Farley allowed the children to run wild until they were old enough to be sent to the big public school. Rosie used to wear a patched slip of dingy material. The wisp of disordered hair was caught up with a black string. She had the usual affinity for dirt. Her mother never kept her in hand. Her father joked with her and told her Irish goblin stories and was a good playmate, but he never took himself seriously as a parent. She never had any home "training." Certainly she was never "reared."

So why did she pick up into a neat and careful Miss who read books that were new to Pitkin Street? After she finished at the grammar school she was a salesgirl, and then she took up short-hand. She bought her own clothing and had a bank-book.

At twenty she was the only member of the family who had ready money when Tommy, caught up for beating a man with a billiard-cue, had to pay a fine of twenty-five dollars or go to the bridewell. Rosie went to the station and paid the fine. Mrs. Farley wept before, during, and after the trial, protesting that it was the shame of her life that her son should be "in prison." John Farley was gloomily disgraced by the affair and told Tommy that he would have to pay his sister every cent. He has not paid it as yet.

Tommy had grown up in Pitkin Street, as Rosie had. The two attended the same school and were allowed an equal start, such as it was. Tommy, at twenty-seven, is a slouching ruffian who stands at the corner with other members of the "Terry gang," drinks as often as he can, and works as seldom as possible. Rosie, at twenty-four, is a delectable creature, who knows what clothes to wear and how to carry herself. She earns a salary of $15 a week as a stenographer, is prized by her employers, pointed out by all of Pitkin Street, and especially respected and held in awe by John Farley and his wife. All the wayward young girls of Pitkin Street who steal out of evenings to join the rowdy young men are told to observe Rosie Farley, who never does such things. Rosie sets the styles for the street—no flaunting white feathers and gay ribbons, but the trimmest of cloth suits in winter and shirt-waist effects in summer. The over-grown boys who went to school with her touch their hats uneasily when she passes and comment in whispers. That is all. They simply admire her at a distance.

To John Farley it is an unending surprise that he is the father of the wonderful Rosie. She is the ruler of the household and has been ever since a certain Saturday night in June.

John Farley seldom drank too much except on Saturday night, when it was his habit to come home in an excited and confused state of mind and make long speeches to Mrs. Farley, who would weep. The woman was emotional by nature. She loved strange funerals and death-bed stories and family griefs.

When John Farley was in drink he would declaim of his wife's unworthiness, of her improvidence, of her neglect of household duties. The more she moaned and sobbed and lamented the fact of her birth the more sweeping and eloquent was his attack. Her demonstrative grief seemed to act as a stimulant to his invective. These occasional Saturday night scenes had been enacted ever since Rosie could remember. As a little girl she had lain in bed, trembling at the sounds and feeling a secret shame that she had been born to such parents. Later she had endured the squalls with saintly forbearance. Later still, she wearied of them. She began to understand that her father's Saturday night attack and her mother's responsive weeping made up a kind of ceremonial which had no serious import and was observed solely because it had attained the dignity of a custom.

Her father never quarrelled except after drinking. It seemed that when he came to a certain period of intoxication he had the impulse to go home and deliver the set oration to his wife. Her sufferings were terrible on Saturday evening. On Sunday morning she would be placid and cheerful again.

On the Saturday evening which marked the change of administration, young Mr. Carroll, son of the contractor, had called to see Rosie. They were sitting on the front stoop when John Farley came home through the front gate and went around to the side-door of the house. He walked with his feet far apart and was staring straight ahead with a filmy and unobservant gaze. He was very erect, also, as a man should be when he is quite sober.

Rosie was prepared for what began in the kitchen. John started in on his familiar and highly colored speech depicting the woes of the honest working-man who is married to a lazy and wasteful slattern. The doors and windows were open. This oration threatened to permeate the block.

"Please go home, Mr. Carroll," said Rosie, "I am needed in the house."

Mrs. Farley was sitting beside the kitchen-table, with her

apron rolled into a handkerchief. She was rocking sidewise and wailing mechanically, and there was a rivulet of tears on each cheek.

John Farley was pacing between the table and the stove, making broad and slashing gestures to accompany his fluent vituperation.

"What if I do go and take a drink?" he demanded. "What objection should you have, you poor, mis'able creature? I have me rights and me liberties, which not you or anny one else can deprive me of. Now mind you that! I might as well let me money go for drink as have it thrown away by the likes of you. I'm an industhrus, hard-workin' man six days in the week an'——"

"Father! Stop that!"

John Farley stopped short, with his hand up, and looked in bleary surprise at Rosie, who stood in the doorway, her lips closed tightly and her eyes squinted with determination.

"Rosie, I've put up with that woman for years an' y'know that as well——"

"Hush! I don't want to hear another word out of you. Let me tell you something. Unless you and mother stop this nonsense, I'm going to leave this house and never come back."

"Oh, Rosie, poor soul, if you on'y knew—" faltered Mrs. Farley.

"I know that you are a fool, that's what I know for one thing, mother. Why do you pay any attention to him when he comes home in this condition and begins this silly talk. I've heard it for years and I'm thoroughly tired of it. Hereafter, father, you do all of your talking at the saloon and then come home and go to bed."

John Farley smacked his lips and tried to put himself into an attitude of authority.

"Rosie, you mustn't int'fere," he said, and he made a short gesture as of brushing something aside.

"Father!"—he jumped when she said it. "Right through this door and to your room! And not another word out of you to-night."

"I'll do it as a favor to you, Rosie," he said, teetering slightly as he turned to make for the door. "I'll do it for you, but I want't unde'stood I——"

"Very well, we will discuss that part of it in the morning."

Then she turned to her mother, whose grief had settled down to a low, bubbling tremolo with equi-distant gusty sighs that seemed to lift the good woman from the chair.

"He's abused me—this way—time after time, until—I just think sometimes—I can't stand it any longer," said Mrs. Farley, through the folds of her damp apron.

"Stop that sniffling!" commanded Rosie. "Don't you know that you encourage him to carry on that way? You ought to know it by this time. I think this house needs a manager."

So from that evening Rosie became manager and there was a reform administration. The Saturday-night outbreaks ceased. Rosie changed the marketing-list and taught her father to eat new kinds of food. She bought her mother's dresses and made Mrs. Farley presentable in spite of herself. It was Rosie who pitched out the chromos and the jig-saw brackets and the yellow-plush sofa and brought in rugs and water-colours. Rosie took charge of her father's tin box and directed the payments to the building and loan association. It was Rosie who had the house painted.

The climax of the revolution came when Rosie announced that Tommy would be expected to pay board if he remained at home. He could get work at the mantel factory, and Rosie told him that $3.50 a week would be a great help in the financing of the household. Tommy was much aggrieved at the demand, and his mother rather sympathised with him. She told Rosie not to be too hard on a "slip of a boy." But the "slip of a boy" was past twenty-five when Rosie gave him the stern alternative of earning his living or starving to death. So Tommy is working intermittently, much against his will.

On Saturday night, when John Farley gets the customary glass too much, he does not go home to lacerate the humid sensibilities of Mrs. Farley. When he feels his vocal strength demanding an outlet and he knows that he must gesticulate in order to relieve himself, he gives the company in the Bridgeport Buffet a serious speech on the subject of Rosie, most wondrous of her sex.

Dubley, '89

Mr. Dubley, '89, was flattered to receive an invitation to attend the annual dinner of the Beverly alumni and respond to the toast, "College Days." Mr. Dubley, class of '89, in his days pointed out as a real ornament to the campus, had allowed his interest in college matters to ooze away from him. He had been in Chicago three years and had not attended an annual dinner, but now, being invited to speak, he felt it his duty to step in and accept the honor.

See Mr. Dudley in his room at night—writing, writing. He was writing about "College Days"—but he erased much more than he wrote. When he had completed a sentence he would read it aloud to make sure that it had the swing and cadence so pleasing to the ear.

One week before the dinner and Mr. Dubley's speech regarding "College Days" was a finished thing. It had been typewritten, with broad spaces, and there were parenthetical reminders such as: (Pause), (full breath), (gesture with right hand), etc. Mr. Dubley had witnessed the pitiable flunks resulting from a state of unpreparedness, and he was not going to rely upon momentary inspiration. He was going to rehearse every part of his speech, and when he arose to respond to the toast "College Days" that speech would be a part of his mental fibre.

If Mr. Dubley talked mutteringly as he hid behind his newspaper on the elevated train or made strange gestures as he hurried along Dearborn Street, it was not to be inferred that Mr. Dubley had lost his mind. He was practising—that is all.

The speech:

"Mr. President and Gentlemen: The toastmaster has told you that I am to speak of 'College Days,' a subject that must arouse the tenderest and sweetest memories in the bosom of every one here. When I look about me and see all these faces beaming with good-fellowship and fraternal love, I realise that there are no ties as lasting as those that we form in the bright days of our youth, within the college halls. No matter what experiences may befall us after we have gone out into the world, we can always look back with pleasure on the days that we spent in college.

" *'You may break, you may shatter, the vase if you will,*
But the scent of the roses will cling 'round it still.'

"I sometimes think that in the rush and hurry of business life, here in this great metropolis, we make a serious mistake in neglecting to keep up the friendships formed in college. I tell you, fellow-alumni, we ought to extend a helping hand to every man who comes to this city from old Beverly. Let us keep alive the holy torch ignited at the altar of youthful loyalty.

"The enthusiasm manifested here this evening proves that you indorse what I have just said. I know that your hearts beat true to our dear alma mater; that other institutions, larger and more pretentious, perhaps, can never hold the same place in your affections.

"Oh, that we might again gather on the campus in the same company that was once so dear to us, there to sing the old college songs, to feel the hand-clasp of our college mates, and listen to the sweet chiming of the chapel bell. These are memories to be treasured. In the years to come we shall find that they are the brightest pages in life's history.

"Gentlemen, I have no wish to tire you. There are other speakers to follow me. In conclusion I merely wish to relate a little anecdote which is suggested to me by the opening remarks of our worthy toastmaster. It seems there was an Irishman who had been in this country but a few days, and he was looking for work, so he said to himself one morning: 'Begob, Oi think Oi'll go down to the dock to see if I can't be afther gettin' a job unloadin' a ship.' So he went down to the dock, but couldn't get any work. While he was standing there looking down into the water, a man in a diving-suit came up through the waves and climbed up on the dock. Pat looked at him in great surprise and said: 'Begob, if Oi'd known where to get a suit loike that, I'd have walked over mesilf.' "

During the gale of laughter which was to follow this story, Mr. Dubley would sit down.

Now, in order that he might not become confused as to the order of his paragraphs and to guard against the remote possibility of his forgetting some part of the address, Mr. Dubley had the opening words of each paragraph jotted down on a card, to which he might refer if necessary:

The president has told, etc.

I sometimes think, etc.

The enthusiasm manifested, etc.

Oh, that we might, etc.

Gentlemen, I have no wish, etc.

The annual dinner of the Beverly alumni was an unqualified success.

Three tables were filled. Two of these were long tables joining a short transverse table, at which sat the chairman and the speakers. Dubley, '89, was at this head table.

Dinner came on with a great clatter. The mandolin orchestra played "coon" songs and the young men bellowed the choruses. An ex-star of the football team was carried thrice round the table on the billowing shoulders of his friends, who chanted and rah-rahed and stepped high.

Mr. Dubley, '89, who was dieting and abstaining, in order that he might be in good voice and have possession of his faculties when the critical moment came, began to suspect that the assemblage was in no mood to give serious attention to the memories of college days. His fellow-alumni sat low in their chairs, with their white fronts very convex, and pounded the tables rhythmically, causing the small coffee-cups to jump and jingle.

Cigars succeeded cigarettes. A blue fog obscured the far end of the double perspective of long tables, and the hurrah was unabated.

The chairman pounded on the table.

"I am glad," he shouted, "to see such a large and disorderly mob here this evening. (*Cheers.*) I understand that Mr. Dubley of the class of '89 has something to say to you, and I will now call on him."

And Mr. Dubley arose. The clamorous applause helped to encourage him. He took a drink of water.

A voice: "What is the gentleman's name, please?"

The chairman: "Dubley—this is Mr. Dubley of the class of '89."

A voice: "Never heard of him before." (*Laughter.*)

Dubley: "Mr. President and gentlemen."

A voice: " 'Mr. President *and* gentlemen'?"

Another voice: "Yes—why this distinction?"

Dubley (*Smiling feebly*): "Of course—you understand—when I say 'Mr. President and gentlemen' I don't mean to insinuate that the president is not a gentleman. I think he is a gentleman."

A voice: "You *think* he is?"

Dubley: "The toastmaster has told you that I am to speak of 'College Days'."

A voice: "I didn't hear him."

Dubley: "Well, he—ah—should have announced that as the subject of my toast. (*Cries of "All right," "Go ahead," "Make good."*) —'College Days', a subject that must arouse the tenderest and sweetest memories in the bosom of every one here." (*Applause.*)

A voice: "Say, this fellow's eloquent." (*Laughter.*)

Dubley: "Tenderest and sweetest memories in the bosom of every one here."

A voice: "No encores."

Another voice: "You said that once."

Dubley: "Pardon me; I—ah——"

A voice: "Go ahead! you're all right—maybe."

Dubley: "When I look around me and see all these faces beaming with good-fellowship and fraternal love I——"

Grand chorus: "Ah-h-h-h-h!"

Dubley: "I say, when I look around——"

A voice: "That's twice you've looked around."

Dubley: "I realise that there are no ties as lasting as those that we form in the bright days of our youth within the college halls. (*Cries of "Good boy" and "Right you are, old rox."*) No matter what experiences may befall us——"

Distant voice: "Mr. Toastmaster! Mr. Toastmaster!"

Chairman: "Well, what is it?"

Distant voice: "There are several of us down at this end of the table who did not catch the gentleman's name. He is making a good speech, and we want to know who he is—let go of my coat!"

The Chairman: "Gentlemen, I will announce for the third time that the speaker who now has the floor is Mr. Harold Dubley of the class of '89, sometimes known as the boy orator of Danville."

A voice: "Harold's such a sweet name."

The Chairman: "I may add that Mr. Dubley has prepared his speech with great care and I hope you'll give him your quiet attention." (*Cries of "All right!" and "Let 'er go!"*)

Dubley (*hesitatingly*):

" 'You may break, you may shatter, the vase if you will,
But the scent of the roses will cling round it still.' "

A voice: "Oh, Lizzie!" (*Prolonged howls.*)

Dubley: "I sometimes think——"

A voice: "You don't look it." (*Renewed laughter.*)

Dubley: "I say, I sometimes think——"

A voice: "Did anybody else ever say it?"

Dubley: "—that in the rush and hurry of business life here in the great metropolis we make a serious mistake in neglecting to keep up the friendships formed in college. (*Indian yell. Some one throws a stalk of celery at Dubley.*) Ah—let us keep alive the holy torch ignited at the altar of youthful loyalty."

A voice: "Mr. Toastmaster!"

The Chairman: "What is it?"

A voice: "I propose three cheers for the holy torch." (*Tremendous cheering and laughter.*)

Dubley: "The enthusiasm manifested here this evening proves that you indorse what I have just said."

A voice: "You haven't said anything yet." (*Cries of "Order!" and "Give him a chance."*)

Dubley: "I know that your hearts—I know that your hearts——"

One of the rioters (*arising*): "Mr. Toastmaster, I move you that Mr. Jubley or Gubley or whatever his name is, be directed to omit all anatomical references. He should remember that there are gentlemen present."

The Chairman: "I have every confidence in Mr. Dubley's sense of propriety and must ask him to continue."

Dubley (*hesitating and referring to his card*): "Oh—Oh that we might—might again gather on the campus——"

A voice: "Wouldn't that be nice?"

Dubley: "—in the same company that was once so dear to us, there to sing the old college songs, to——"

A voice: "Mr. Toastmaster!"

The Chairman: "What is it?"

The voice: "I suggest that Mr. Bubley sing one of those college songs to which he refers with so much feeling."

The Chairman: "Again I will inform the company that the speaker's name is not Bubley, but Dubley."

A voice: "With the accent on the 'Dub'."

The Chairman: "Mr. Dubley has promised to sing a song if you will permit him to finish his speech." (*Cries of "All right!" "Go ahead."*)

Dubley (*Once more referring to his card*): "Gentlemen, I have no wish to tire you. (*Cries of "Hear! hear!"*) There are other speakers——"

A voice: "You *bet* there are!"

Dubley: "Er—in conclusion, I merely wish to relate a little anecdote (*Cries of "Ah-h-h-h!"*) which is suggested to me by the opening remarks of our worthy toastmaster. (*Laughter.*) It seems there was an Irishman (*Groans*) who had been in this country but a few days and he was looking for work." (*Loud laughter.*)

The Chairman: "I will have to ask the gentlemen to come to order. Mr. Dubley hasn't finished his story yet."

Dubley: "As I say, this Irishman was looking for work, so he said to himself one morning, 'Begob, Oi think Oi'll go down be the dock to see if I can't be after getting a job un——"

A voice: " 'ster Toastmaster!"

The Chairman: "What is it?"

The voice: "A point of order."

The Chairman: "State your point."

The voice: "The gentleman is telling an Irish story with a Swedish dialect."

The Chairman: "The point is well taken. If Mr. Dubley wishes to go ahead with his anecdote, he will please use an Irish dialect."

Dubley (*On the verge of collapse*): "Well, Mr. Toastmaster, the story's nearly over. (*Cries of "Hooray!"*) All there was to it is that while the Irishman was at the dock he saw a diver in a diving-suit come up out of the water and he thought, of course—I should have told you that this Irishman had lately come over from the old country—then—well—he saw the diver and he thought the diver had walked over from Ireland, so he said——" (*General uproar, during which Dubley dodges a French roll. Some one pulls him into a chair.*)

Dubley: "But I hadn't finished my story."

The man next to him: "Yes, you had."

Although the toastmaster referred to Mr. Dubley's speech in very complimentary terms, Dubley will always have his doubts.

Mr. Lindsay on "San Jewan"

It was at the breakfast-table that Mr. Scott Lindsay, a veteran of the real war, read something about the anniversary of the battle of San Juan and began to rattle the paper.

"Now, now!" said Mrs. Lindsay, calmly, for she knew his tantrums.

"Great grief, mother!" he exclaimed, looking across the table at his wife. "Here's somethin' that'd make old Sherman turn over in his grave. They're goin' to celebrate the anniversary of the battle of San Jewan. *Thunderation!* The *battle* of San Jewan! BATTLE! Gosh, all fish-hooks! BATTLE! Say, if the old boys that 'uz with the Army o' the Tennessee ever started in to celebrate the anniversary of every durned little popgun skirmish like that battle o' San Jewan, we wouldn't do nothin' but celebrate, day in and day out, from one year's end to another. We'd have to git up in the night and annyverserate. *Battle!* Battle nothin'! W'y, around Vicksburg there we used to roll out in the mornin' an' fight three or four o' them battles just to whet our appetites. We didn't call 'em battles, though. We knew the difference between a battle and a ras'berry festival."

"Oh, well, father, you must make some allowances," said Mrs. Lindsay. "These boys don't remember the other war."

"I guess they don't—I just good an' guess they don't. If they did, they wouldn't be steppin' so high. There's a blamed sight o' difference between chasin' some runt of a dago with a white feather in each hand an' chasin' a six-foot Johnny Reb that jus' raises up on his everlastin' hind legs an' comes at you like a runaway horse, breathin' smoke out of his nose an' ears, by gory, an' yellin' like an Injun. It's easy enough to chase anything that runs the other way, but this hero job's got its drawbacks when the other feller gits it into his head that *he* wants to do the chasin' an' swoops out o' the woods like an Ioway cyclone, by gosh, pumpin' lead into you till you git too heavy to run. Battle! When we had 'em stacked up till we couldn't see over 'em, an' every rigiment 'uz whittled down to a company an' our flags 'uz blown into carpet rags an' the blood got so deep it wet the ammanition in the waggons, we used to begin to *suspect* that we'd had a battle. Somethin' a little less argymentative than that we called a skirmish. Anything the size o' this San Jewan *basket-meetin'* we didn't keep no tally of at all. That kind o' come under the head o' target-practice."

"I wouldn't be too hard on 'em, father. They say these boys fought real well down there in Cuby."

"Well, to see 'em cavortin' around town here in their cowboy hats and gassin' in front of every store, you'd think, by cracky, that every one of 'em had chawed up a thousand o' them Spanish generals, whiskers an' all. You take some old codger that crawled through them swamps for four years, dodgin' minie-balls and nothin' to keep him alive but hardtack an' hot slough-water, an' he ain't in it no more with one o' these cussed little whipper-snappers, by ginger, that—well, you ought to heard old Cap Nesbit the other night after post-meetin'. He made a few remarks about these kid soldiers that wouldn't pass muster in a crowd o' women, but they was satisfyin' to *me*."

"I don't see why Cap Nesbit wants to pick onto these boys," said Mrs. Lindsay. "I think they deserve a lot o' credit for enlistin' an' goin' down there in that hot country to fight."

"Enlistin's all right an' fightin's all right, *if* you *do* it. I don't begrudge no man the credit of goin' out an' fightin' for his country. These boys done well as far as they went, but I don't want no kid to tell me what war is till he's been through one. These young fellers got a sniff o' blood, and now they think they've been through the slaughter-house. There's old Dan Bailey that got shot so often he didn't mind it at all toward the last, laid in Andersonville till he was a rack of bones, come home here lookin' like a corpse and ain't seen a well day since, and he ain't as big a man in this town to-day as that grandson o' his that went down there to Porty Rico an' laid in a hammock for six months, smokin' cigarettes. He's what they call a hero now—had an ice-cream reception for him when he come home, didn't they? I don't rickollect that anybody had an ice-cream reception for old Dan when *he* come home. Heroes wuzn't quite so gosh blamed scarce about that time. Nobody paid any attention to 'em. They used to ship 'em in here by the carload, and most of 'em went right on through town an' out to the graveyard. W'y, these boys, they rode down to that dress-parade in Cuby in sleepin'-cars! With a nigger to brush 'em off an' bring ice-water! Great Jehoshaphat! I'd like to seen somebody ask old Griggs for a sleepin'-car. I'd like to heard what he'd say. Sleepin'-cars! We wuz tickled to death to git box-cars, cattle-cars—anything on wheels. We didn't need no porter to brush our cloze, for the darned good reason that we didn't have no cloze to brush. Then there wuz all that talk about em-bammed beef. We'd a been mighty glad to git it—embammed, petrified, mouldy, or any other way. We thought we wuz lucky if we could git a hunk o' salt pork to drop in with the beans now an' then. We wuzn't out on no moonlight ex-cursion, playin' tag with a lot o' tambourine-players. We wuz out in the underbrush, dad ding my buttons, havin' it out with the toughest lot o' human panthers that ever wore cloze. An' yit, like as not, if we go to breakin' in on this San Jewan celebration, we'll git a back seat in the gallery. We ain't heroes. No! W'y, on Decoration Day these kids marched in front, every one of 'em puffed up like a toad in a thunder-storm—bigger man that old Grant, as the feller says. Now, they're goin' to celebrate the annyversary of San Jewan. Sufferin' Cornelius! There wuz another likely skirmish about the same time o' year. *Gettysburg,* I think they called it. Wonder why somebody don't celebrate *that!*"

MORE FABLES

Preface

This little book is not supposed to contain any new information. It is made up of plain observations concerning people who live just around the corner. If the reader will bear in mind that *only* the people who live around the corner are discussed in this volume, there will be no chance for painful misunderstandings. I have no desire to rub the wrong way anyone who proves his true friendship by purchasing a copy of this Work. It may be advisable to explain that these Fables are written in the colloquial American language. The vocabulary employed is one that has become familiar to the ear, although it is seldom seen on the printed page. In other words, this volume contains a shameless amount of slang. If any part of it is unintelligible to the reader, he should be glad that he has escaped what seems to be an epidemic.

THE AUTHOR.
(from *People You Know,*
(1902))

The Periodical Souse, the Never-Again Feeling and the Ride on the Sprinkling Cart

Once there was an Indian who had a Way of putting on all his Feathers and breaking out of the Reservation.

For three Weeks at a Stretch he gave a Correct Imitation of the Shining Light who passes the Basket and superintends the Repairs on the Parsonage. He was entitled to a Mark of 100 for Deportment. With his Meals he drank a little Polly. After Dinner he smoked one Perfecto and then, when he had put in a frolicsome Hour or so with the North American Review, he crawled into the Hay at 9.30 P.M.

At last he accumulated a Sense of Virtue that was hard to carry around. He was proud of himself when he counted up the number of days during which he had stuck to the Straight and Narrow. It seemed to him that he deserved a Reward. So he decided to buy himself a little Present, something costing about 15 cents. He picked out a First-Class Place where they had Electric Fans and Pictures by the Old Masters. He poured out a Workingman's Size—the kind that makes the Barkeep stop wiping up and look unfriendly for a Moment or two.

Then he remembered that a Bird cannot fly with one Wing, so he gently raised the Index Finger and gave the Prescription Clerk a Look, which in the Sign Language means, "Repeat the Dose."

It is an Historical Fact that when a Man falls backward from the Water Wagon he always lands in a Crowd. The full Stage Setting, the Light Effects and the Red Fire were all ready to make it a Spectacular Affair. Just after he had mowed away No. 2 and had stopped worrying about the Winter's Coal, he began to meet Friends who were dying of Thirst. Then the atmosphere began to be curdled with High Balls and Plymouth Sours and Mint Smashes, and he was telling a Shoe Drummer that a lot of People who had been knocking him would probably be working for him before the Year was out.

Then he found himself in a four-oared Cablet and the Sea became very Rough. There was something out of Whack with the Steering Gear, for instead of bringing up at his Boarding House he found himself at another Rum Parlor. The Man who owned the Place had lost the Key and could not lock up. Here he met several Delegates to a State Convention of a Fraternal Order having for its Purpose the uplifting of Mankind. They wore Blue Badges and were fighting to get their Money into the Cash Register. In a little while he and a redheaded Delegate were up by the Cigar Counter singing, "How can I bear to leave thee?" He put in an Application for Membership and then the next Picture that came out of the Fog was a Chop Suey Restaurant and everybody breaking Dishes.

Soon after, the Lights went out and when he came back to Earth he was lying the wrong way of his Bed with Blue Badges all over him, trying to swallow a Bath Towel, which he afterward discovered was his Tongue. By getting a Leverage under his Head he managed to pry it up and then he sat on the edge of the Bed and called himself Names. He had nothing left over except the Cards given to him by the Brothers from up State somewhere. He had a dim and sneaking Recollection that he had given his address and Phone Number to the whole Tribe and begged them to look him up.

"Not any more in Mine," said he, as he held a Towel under the Faucet. "Not for all of Morgan's would I look at any more of that Essence of Trouble. I wonder if I'll live through the Morning."

That Day he lived on Bromo and Ice, and the only Satisfaction this Life offered was the Fact that he was a Reformed Man.

On the Second Day he could look at Solid Food without having a Spasm. His Hair stopped pulling and he began to speak to the People he met. When asked to step out for a little while, he lost his Temper and made a little Talk on the Subject, proving conclusively that there was Nothing in it.

As he walked homeward in the Dusk he passed the Clubs and Cafés where those who Drank were rounding up and he felt sorry for them.

"Why can't they pass it up, the same as I do?" he asked himself. "Ah, if only they knew how much more Fun it is to be Respectable."

It was an actual Mystery to him that any one could dally with a Dry Martini while there was a Hydrant on every Corner.

On the third Day he was cracking his Whip and begging People to get up on the Wagon with him. And he said it was a Queer Thing, but he couldn't bear the Sight of it.

While on the fourth Evening he confessed to some nice People he met at a Church Social that at one time he had allowed himself to be coaxed into taking an occasional Nip but he reasoned it all out and decided it was a Bad Thing and simply Chopped it right off. They told him it was wonderful how much Will Power he had and asked him if he ever felt the Old Craving coming back on him, and he said he could see it splashing all around him and not have the faintest Desire to dip in.

He was so stuck on himself that he went around to call on all his Friends who kept it on the Table so that he could wave it to one side and tell how he despised it. He sat there and pitied those who were inhaling it. Every Morning when he arose he would throw kisses to himself in the Glass and exclaim: "Aha! The Head as clear as a Bell this A.M. I'll bet I'm the cleanest and nicest Young Fellow in this Town. Any Girl that picks out a Sober and Steady Man such as I am will certainly be showing good Judgment."

As Narrated at the Beginning, for three weeks he worked hard at the Job of being an Abstainer. And at last he accumulated a Sense of Virtue that weighed over 200 Pounds. He knew that he was entitled to a Reward, so he decided to buy himself a little Present. Just a wee Reminder of by-gone Days and then back to Sarsaparilla. But he fell into a Crowd. There was another State Convention. It had been arranged for him so that he could get a Fresh Start.

Moral: *Life is a Series of Relapses and Recoveries.*

The One or Two Points of Difference Between Learning and Learning How

In a Red School-House back in the Web-Foot District, it was the Custom to have a Debate every Friday Afternoon. The much-mooted Question as to which does the greater Damage, Fire or Water, had been carefully gone over by the Squabs. Also who was the heftier Proposition, Napoleon or Washington? But the original Stand-by was as follows: "Resolved, that Education is better than Wealth."

The Corporate Interest got many a Whack here in the Knowledge Works. Most of the Children wanted to grow up and be like Galileo. They claimed that mere Wealth could not purchase Happiness. The only genuine Peace of Mind came from being able to call off the Geological Periods with the Eyes closed.

Here in this little Brain Hatchery were two Kids who were not Mates. One was named Otis and the other was Bradford, or Brad for Short. Otis was the Boy who took the Affirmative side on Friday Afternoon. Ote firmly believed that Learning was the most valuable Asset that a Man could tuck away. Brad was for the Money End of the Game, but when he got up to make his Talk his Vocabulary would become jammed up and caught crossways in the Flue and teacher would motion him back to his Seat. Otis, however, could tell in well-chosen Phrases why the Scholar was a better and happier Man than the Millionaire and so he always received the Vote of the Judges.

Now, Brad was done up but unconvinced. He could not stand up before the District School and tell why it was good policy to corral the Coin, but he had a secret Hunch that it would be no Disgrace for him to go out and do the best he could. Brad had a bull-dog Jaw and large blood-shot Hands and a Neck-Band somewhat larger than his Hat-Band. He jumped the Stockade when they started to teach him Botany. He weighed 180 and he thought he was too large to sit around and count the Petals of the Ox-Eye Daisy when he might be out selling Lightning Rods to the Yaps and making jug-handled Contracts. Accordingly he Dug.

"Bradford is making a great Mistake," said Otis, as he saw his Friend tear from the Institution of Learning. "In order to get a few worldly Chattels right at the jump, he sacrifices his Diploma. I shall be more Foxy. I shall go right on through the High School and then I shall attend College and get a Degree. When I have taken my Degree then I will be the human *It.* My scholarly Attainments and polished Manner will get me past the Door and into the Inner Circle of the Hot Potatoes. As for Bradford, although it is possible that he shall have combed up a little Currency he will be a mere ordinary, sordid Business Man—not one-two-seven when he tries to stack up against one who has just been delivered of a Thesis on the Correlated Phenomena of Unconscious Cerebration."

While Brad was out in the back Townships short-changing the Farmers and buying 8 per cent. Mortgages, Otis was working his way through College and living on Oatmeal except on Holidays and then Prunes. He was getting round-shouldered and wore Specs and was all gaunted up, but he never weakened. He was pulling for the Laurel Wreath of Scholarship, or in other words, the Degree. After humping it for 4 years he passed his final Exam and the Faculty decided that he was a Bachelor of Arts.

That was the Day when he had the Laugh on Brad.

In the meantime, Bradford had been choking various People and taking it away from them. He had four Salesmen under him and had butted into the Firm, but he was still shy on Botany.

Inasmuch as Otis had been one of the brightest Men in his Class he was offered a position as Instructor in the College at a Salary of $55 a Month with a promise of $5 raise at the end of five years, if he lived. Otis accepted, because the Outside World did not seem to be clamoring for his Services, even though he was an Authority on the Mesozoic Period and knew all the Diatomes by their First Names.

Often while he was burning the Midnight Oil and grinding out Jaw-Breakers, so as to qualify for the Master's Degree, he reflected as follows. "It is true that Brad is making it Hand over Fist and wears $6 Shirts and rides in a State-Room on the Pullman, but he is not a Bachelor of Arts. And some day when he is a Multi-Millionaire I can still look down on him, for then I shall be a Master of Arts. I have known since Childhood that Education is more desirable than Paltry Gold. Although the newspapers and the General Public do not seem to be with me to any Extent, it is better to hob-nob with the Binomial Theorem than to dally with the Champagne Supper."

In due time the Faculty gave the Degree of M.A. to what was left of Otis and still his Ambition was not satisfied. He wanted to land a Doctor's Degree. He knew that any one who aspired to this Eminent Honor had to be a Pippin. But he hoped that he could make some Contribution to the World of Thought that would jar the whole Educational System and help him to climb to the topmost Pinnacle of Human Greatness.

Professor Otis did the Dig Act year after year. At the age of 49 he was still M.A. and owned a House with a Mortgage on it. In the Meantime there had been revolutionary Changes in the World of Finance. Everything on Earth had been put into a Pool. Each Smooth Citizen who had something that was of no particular use to him went to work and Capitalized it. Brad closed out his Interests for so much Money that any one else would have been ashamed to take it. Then he and some other Buccaneers went down to Wall Street to have fun with several dignified Gentlemen whom Brad described as Them Fly Eastern Mugs. They succeeded in putting the Skids under a number of Persons who did not care to meet them Socially.

When Brad walked around in his Million Dollar Hut he had to step high to avoid stumbling over Bundles of the Long Green; but he never had made any further headway with his Botany.

It happened one Day that Brad was out Moting and he dropped in at the College where his Boyhood Friend was now the Professor of Dipsicology and Plamazzus.

"This is a likely-looking Plant," said Brad, as he sized up the Campus. "I like to encourage these Joints because they help to keep a lot of Young Fellows away from Business Offices. I find that I have here in my Vest-Pocket a measly $50,000 that I have overlooked in changing my Clothes. Give it to the Main Cheese and tell him to have a Laboratory on me."

When the News got out all the sis-boom-ah Boys gave a Parade in their Nighties. The Faculty called a Special Meeting and made Brad a Doctor of Philosophy.

Next Year he put up for a Gym and they made him a Doctor of Divinity.

The Year Following he handed them a Telescope and became an LL.D.

Every time he coughed he was made some new kind of Doctor.

In fact, for a Man with a 6-¼ Hat who did not know the difference between the Pistil and the Stamen he was the most learned Thing in Seven States. Professor Otis was crowded into the Ditch. Sometimes he wonders which of the two has the nub end of the Argument that started in the Red School-House.

Moral: *The Longest Way Around is the Shortest Way to the University Degree.*

The Attenuated Attorney Who Rang In the Associate Counsel

Once there was a sawed-off Attorney who had studied until he was Bleary around the Eyes and as lean as a Razor-Back. He knew the Law from Soup to Nuts, but much learning had put him a little bit to the Willies. And his Size was against him. He lacked Bellows.

He was an inconspicuous little Runt. When he stood up to Plead, he came a trifle higher than the Chair. Of the 90 pounds he carried, about 45 were Gray Matter. He had Mental Merchandise to burn but no way of delivering it.

When there was a Rally or some other Gabfest on the Bills, the Committee never asked him to make an Address. The Committee wanted a Wind-Jammer who could move the Leaves on a Tree 200 feet distant. The dried-up Lawyer could write Great Stuff that would charm a Bird out of a Tree, but he did not have the Tubes to enable him to Spout. When he got up to Talk, it was all he could do to hear himself. The juries used to go to sleep on him. He needed a Megaphone. And he had about as much Personal Magnetism as an Undertaker's Assistant.

The Runt lost many a Case because he could not Bark at the Jury and pound Holes in a Table. His Briefs had been greatly admired by the Supreme Court. Also it was known that he could draw up a copper-riveted Contract that would hold Water, but as a Pleader he was a Pickerel.

At one time he had an Important Suit on hand, and he was Worried, for he was opposed by a couple of living Gas

Engines who could rare up and down in front of a yap jury for further Orders.

"I have the Law on my Side," said the Runt. "Now if I were only Six-Feet-Two with a sole-leather Thorax, I could swing the Verdict."

While he was repining, in came a Friend of his Youth, named Jim.

This Jim was a Book-Agent. He was as big as the Side of a House. He had a Voice that sounded as if it came up an Elevator Shaft. When he folded his Arms and looked Solemn, he was a colossal Picture of Power in Repose. He wore a Plug Hat and a large Black Coat. Nature intended him for the U. S. Senate, but used up all the Material early in the Job and failed to stock the Brain Cavity.

Jim had always been at the Foot of the Class in School. At the age of 40 he spelled Sure with an Sh and sank in a Heap when he tried to add 8 and 7. But he was a tall Success as a Book Peddler, because he learned his Piece and the 218 Pounds of Dignified Superiority did the Rest.

Wherever he went, he commanded Respect. He could go into a strange Hotel, and sit down at the Breakfast Table and say: "Please pass the Syrup," in a Tone that had all the majestic Significance of an Official Utterance. He would sit there in silent Meditation. Those who sized up that elephantine Form and noted the Gravity of his Countenance and the fluted Wrinkles on his high Brow, imagined that he was pondering on the Immortality of the Soul. As a matter of fact, Jim was wondering whether he would take Ham or Bacon with his Eggs.

Jim had the Bulk and the awe-inspiring Front. As long as he held to a Napoleonic Silence he could carry out the Bluff. Little Boys tip-toed when they came near him, and Maiden Ladies sighed for an introduction. Nothing but a Post-Mortem Examination would have shown Jim up in his True Light. The midget Lawyer looked up in Envy at his mastodonic Acquaintance and sighed.

"If I could combine my Intellect with your Horse-Power,

I would be the largest Dandelion in the Legal Pasture," he said.

Then a Happy Idea struck him amidships.

"Jim, I want you to be my Associate Counsel," he said. "I understand, of course, that you do not know the difference between a Caveat and a Caviar Sandwich, but as long as you keep your Hair combed the way it is now and wear that Thoughtful Expression, you're just as good as the whole Choate Family. I will introduce you as an Eminent Attorney from the East. I will guard the Law Points and you will sit there and Dismay the Opposition by looking Wise."

So when the Case came up for Trial, the Runt led the august Jim into the Court Room and introduced him as Associate Counsel. A Murmur of Admiration ran throughout the Assemblage when Jim showed his Commanding Figure, a Law Book under his Arm and a look of Heavy Responsibility on his Face. Old Atlas, who carries the Globe on his Shoulders, did not seem to be in it with this grand and gloomy Stranger.

For two hours Jim had been rehearsing his Speech. He arose.

"Your Honor," he began.

At the Sound of that Voice, a scared Silence fell upon the Court Room. It was like the Lower Octave of a Pipe Organ.

"Your Honor," said Jim, "we are ready for Trial."

The musical Rumble filled the Spacious Room and went echoing through the Corridors. The Sound beat out through the Open Windows and checked Traffic in the Street. It sang through the Telegraph Wires and lifted every drooping Flag.

The Jurors turned Pale and began to quiver. Opposing Counsel were as white as a Sheet. Their mute and frightened Faces seemed to ask, "What are we up against?"

Jim sat down and the Trial got under way.

Whenever Jim got his Cue he arose and said, "Your Honor and Gentlemen of the Jury, I quite agree with my learned Colleague."

Then he would relapse and throw on a Socrates Frown and

the Other Side would go all to Pieces. Every time Jim cleared his Throat, you could hear a Pin drop. There was no getting away from the dominating Influence of the Master Mind.

The Jury was out only 10 Minutes. When the Verdict was rendered, the Runt, who had provided everything except the Air Pressure, was nearly trampled under foot in the general Rush to Congratulate the distinguished Attorney from the East. The Little Man gathered up his Books and did the customary Slink, while the False Alarm stood in awful Silence and permitted the Judge and others to shake him by the Hand.

Moral: *An Associate Counsel should weigh at least 200 pounds.*

The Regular Kind of a Place and the Usual Way It Turned Out

Once there was a home-like Beanery where one could tell the Day of the Week by what was on the Table.

The Stroke Oar of this Food Bazaar had been in the Business for 20 years, and she had earned her Harp three times over. The Prune Joke never touched her, and she had herself trained so as not to hear any sarcastic Cracks about the Oleo. She prided herself on the Atmosphere of Culture that permeated the Establishment, and on the Fact that she did not harbor any Improper Characters. A good many Improper Characters came around and sized up the Lay-Out and then blew.

It was a sure-enough Boarding-House, such as many of our Best People know all about even if they won't tell.

The Landlady was doing what she could to discourage the Beef Trust, but she carried a heavy line of Oatmeal. She had Oatmeal to burn and sometimes she did it. And she often remarked that Spinach had Iron in it and was great for the Blood. One of her pet Theories was that Rice contained more

Nutriment than could be found in Spring Chicken, but the Boarders allowed that she never saw a Spring Chicken.

In the Cast of Characters were many of the Old Favorites. There was the lippy Boy with the Williams and Walker Shirts, who knew the Names of all the Ball-Players and could tell when there was a good Variety Show in Town.

Then there was the other kind, with a straw-colored Mustache and a prominent Adam's Apple, who was very careful about his Pronunciation. He belonged to a Social Purity Club that had a Yell. His Idea of a Hurrah was to get in a Parlor with a few Sisters who were under the Age Limit and sing the Bass Part of "Pull for the Shore."

Then there was the Old Boarder. He was the Land-Mark. Having lived in Boarding-Houses and Hotels all his Life, he had developed a Gloom that surrounded him like a Morning Fog. He had a Way of turning Things over with his Fork, as if to say, "Well, I don't know about this." And he never believed anything he saw in the Papers. He said the Papers printed those things just to fill up. The Circassian Princess that brought in the Vittles paid more attention to him than to any one else, because if he didn't get Egg on his Lettuce he was liable to cry all over the Table Cloth.

Then there was the chubby Man who came in every Evening and told what had happened at the Store that Day, and there was a human Ant-Eater who made Puns.

One of the necessary Features of a refined Joint is the Slender Thing who is taking Music and has Mommer along to fight off the Managers and hush the Voice of Scandal. This Boarding-House had one of these Mother-and-Child Combinations that was a Dream. Daughter was full of Kubelik and Josef Hofmann. Away back in the Pines somewhere there was a Father who was putting up for the Outfit. Mother's Job seemed to be to sit around and Root. She was a consistent little Booster. If what Mother said was true, then Effie's Voice was a good deal better than it sounded. She said the Teachers were just crazy about it and all of them agreed that Effie ought to go to Paris or Milan. The slangy Boy with the rag-time Shirt went them one better, and said that *all* of the phoney Melbas in the country ought to pull for the Old Country and wait until they were sent for.

In this same Boarding-House there was a Widow whose husband had neglected to die. Being left all alone in the World she had gone out to make her Way, since which time she had gained about 30 pounds and was considered Great Company by the Young Men.

Necessarily there was a Pale Lady who loved to read, and who stuck to the Patterns that appeared in Godey's Magazine soon after the War.

Then there was the Married Couple, without any Children or Furniture of their own, and the only reason they didn't take a House was that Henry had to be out of Town so often. Henry's Salary had been whooped $500 a Year and she was just beginning to say Gown instead of Dress. She had the Society Column for Breakfast and things looked Dark for Henry.

For many months this conventional Group of ordinary 6-7/8 Mortals had lived in a Rut. At each meal-time they rounded up and mechanically devoured what was doled out to them and folded their Napkins and broke Ranks. Each day was the Duplicate of another and Life had petered down to a Routine.

One Evening just as they had come in for their Vermicelli, a new Boarder glided into their midst. She was a tall Gypsy Queen with about $1,200 worth of Clothes that fit her everywhere and all the time, and she had this watch-me kind of a Walk, the same being a Cue for all the other Girls to get out their Hardware.

When she moved up to the Table and began to distribute a few sample Smiles, so as to indicate the Character of her Work, the musical Team went out with the Tide, the Grass Widow curled up like an Autumn Leaf, the touch-me-not Married Lady dropped into the Scrub Division. The Lady who read was shy a Spoon and afraid to ask for it. The Men were all google-eyed, and the Help was running into Chairs and dropping important parts of the Menu.

Presently the Landlady came in and explained. She said that Mrs. Williams was in the City to shop for a couple of Days, and her Husband would be up on the Night Train. Whereupon five men fell under the Table.

Moral: *Nothing ever happens at a Boarding House.*

The Patient Toiler Who Got It in the Usual Place

Once there was an Office Employee with a Copy-Book Education.

He believed it was his Duty to learn to Labor and to Wait.

He read Pamphlets and Magazine Articles on Success and how to make it a Cinch. He knew that if he made no Changes and never beefed for more Salary, but just buckled down and put in Extra Time and pulled for the House, he would Arrive in time.

The Faithful Worker wanted to be Department Manager. The Hours were short and the Salary large and the Work easy.

He plugged on for many Moons, keeping his Eye on that Roll-Top Desk, for the Manager was getting into the Has-Been Division and he knew there would be a Vacancy.

At last the House gave the old Manager the Privilege of retiring and living on whatever he had saved.

"Ah, this is where Humble Merit gets its Reward," said the Patient Toiler. "I can see myself counting Money."

That very Day the Main Gazooks led into the Office one of the handsomest Tennis Players that ever worked on Long Island and introduced him all around as the new Department Manager.

"I shall expect you to tell Archibald all about the Business," said the Main Gazooks to the Patient Toiler. "You see he has just graduated from Yale and he doesn't know a dum Thing about Managing anything except a Cat-Boat, but his Father is one of our principal Stock-Holders and he is engaged to a Young Woman whose Uncle is at the head of the Trust."

"I had been hoping to get this Job for myself," said the Faithful Worker, faintly.

"You are so valuable as a Subordinate and have shown such an Aptitude for Detail Work that it would be a Shame to waste you on a $5,000 Job," said the Main Gazooks. "Besides you are not Equipped. You have not been to Yale. Your Father is not a Stock-Holder. You are not engaged to a Trust. Get back to your High Stool and whatever Archibald wants to know, you tell him."

Moral: *One who wishes to be a Figure-Head should not Overtrain.*

The Maneuvers of Joel and the Disappointed Orphan Asylum

An old Residenter, who owned a Section of Improved Land, and some Town Property besides, was getting too Feeble to go out and roast the Hired Hands, so he turned the Job over to his Son. This Son was named Joel. He was foolish, the same as a Fox. Any one who got ahead of Joel had to leave a 4:30 Call and start on a Lope. When it came to Skin Games he was the original High-Binder.

Joel took the Old Gentleman aside one Day and said to him: "Father, you are not long for this World, and to save Lawyer Fees and avoid a tie-up in the Probate Court, I think you ought to cut up your Estate your own self, and then you will know it is done Right."

"How had I better divide it?" asked the Old Gentleman.

"You can put the whole Shooting-Match in my Name," suggested Joel. "That will save a lot of Writing. Then if any other Relatives need anything, they can come to me and try to Borrow it."

Joel sent for a cut-rate Shyster, who brought a bundle of Papers tied with Green Braid, and assured the Old Gentleman that the Proceeding was a Mere Formality. When a Legal Wolf wants to work the Do-Do on a Soft Thing, he always springs that Gag about a Mere Formality.

Joel and the Shell-Worker moved the Old Gentleman up to a table in the Front Room and put a Cushion under him and slipped a Pen into his Hand and showed him where to Sign.

After he got through filling the Blank Spaces with his John Hancock, he didn't have a Window to hoist or a Fence to lean on. He was simply sponging on Joel.

This went on for about a Month, and then Joel began to Fret.

"I don't think I am getting a Square Deal," said Joel. "Here is an Ancient Party without any Assets, who lives with me Week in and Week out and doesn't pay any Board. He is getting too Old and Wabbly to do Odd Jobs around the Place, and it looks to me like an awful Imposition."

So he went to the Old Gentleman and said: "Father, I know the Children must annoy you a good deal; they make so much Noise when they play House. Sometimes we want to use the Piano after it is your Bed-Time, and of course that breaks your Rest, so I have been thinking that you would be a lot better off in some Institution where they make a Specialty of looking after Has-Beens. I have discovered a nice, quiet Place. You will live in a large Brick Building, with a lovely Cupola on top. There is a very pretty Lawn, with Flower-Beds, and also an ornamental Iron Fence, so that the Dogs cannot break in and bite you. You will be given a nice Suit of Clothes, the same as all the others are wearing, and if you oversleep yourself in the Morning, a Man will come around and call you."

"In other Words, me to the Poor-House," said the Old Residenter.

"You need not call it that, unless you want to," said Joel. "If you choose, you may speak of it as the Home for Aged Persons who got Foolish with their Fountain Pens."

So Joel put his Father into the Spring Wagon and Hauled him over the Hills to the Charity Pavilion, where all the Old Gentleman had to do was to sit around in the Sun looking at the Pictures in last year's Illustrated Papers and telling himself what a Chump he had been.

But sometimes a Man is not all in, simply because he looks to be wrinkled and doddering. Joel's Father had a Few Thinks coming to him. Although he had been double-crossed and put through the Ropes, he still had a Punch left. He sent for a Lawyer who was even more Crafty than the one employed by Joel and he said to him: "There is a Loop-Hole in every Written Instrument, if one only knows how to find it. I want you to set aside that fool Deed."

Next day the Lawyer came for him in a double-seated Carriage and said, "They forgot to put on a Revenue Stamp and so the Transfer is off."

"And do I get all of my Property back again?" asked the Old Residenter.

"You get half and I get half," was the Reply of the Lawyer.

"Give me mine," said the old Residenter. "I'm from Wisconsin and I want it in the Hand. Whatever I own from this time on, I carry right in my Clothes, and any Relative who separates me from it will have to set his Request to Music." Then he went to a Physician.

"Doc," he says, "they are counting nine on me, but I figure that before I cash in, I have time to spend all that I have. Look me over and tell me how long I would last on a Waldorf diet. I want to gauge my Expenses so as to leave nothing behind for Joel except a Ha-Ha Message and a few Heirlooms."

"If you want to euchre your Family, why don't you leave it to an Orphan Asylum?" suggested the Lawyer.

"Nix the Orphan Asylum," said the Old Residenter. "They would bring a million witnesses to prove that I had been out of my Head for 20 years, and I wouldn't be there to contradict them. I learn that by a singular Coincidence, all the Old People who leave their Money to Hospitals and the like are Mentally Irresponsible. In order to prove that I am in my right Senses, I will Blow mine."

So he went to Palm Beach and other Winter Resorts, at which they charge by the Minute, and wherever he went he gave a faithful Imitation of the Cowboy's first Night in Town.

He bought himself a hot Raglan with a Surcingle around it, and a very doggy line of Cravats, and when he went into the Dining-Room he picked out a Table which commanded a View of the Door at which the Girls came in.

All this time Joel was worried. It seemed a Sin and a Shame for an Old Man to go around spending his own Money.

The Residenter had so much Fun during his Second Time on Earth that he decided to make it a sure-enough Renaissance, so he married a Type-Writer 19 years old, that he met in a Hotel Lobby, and then Joel did go up in the Air.

When she began to pick out Snake Rings and Diamond Wish-Bones, the Old Gentleman saw that there was no longer any Hope for Joel.

Moral: *When buncoing a Relative always be sure that the Knock-Out Drops are Regulation Strength.*

The Married Couple That Went to Housekeeping and Began to Find Out Things

Once there was a Happy Young Pair, each of whom got stuck on the Photograph of the other and thereupon a Marriage was arranged by Mail.

Shortly after taking the Life Risk, they started in to get acquainted. Up to the time that they moved into the Arcadian

Flats and began to take Orders from the Janitor, he never had seen little Sunshine except in her Evening Frock.

He had a sort of sneaking Suspicion that she arose every Morning already attired in a Paris Gown and all the Diamonds.

And she supposed that he went to the Office every Day in his regular John Drew effect with the Folding Hat.

After she began to see Hubby around the Flat in his Other Clothes the Horrible Truth dawned upon her that he was not such a Hot Swell as he had looked to be in the Bunko Photograph.

Sometimes, on Rainy Sundays, he would cut out the Morning Service and decide not to Shave, and then when she got a good long Look at him, she would begin to doubt her own Judgment.

And so far as that is concerned, there were Mornings, after they had been out Late to a Welsh Rabbit Party, when she was a little Lumpy, if any one should ask.

Love's Young Dream was handed several goshawful Whacks about the Time that they started in to get a Line on each other.

For instance, the first Morning at Breakfast it came out that her Idea of a Dainty Snack with which to usher in the Day was a Lettuce Sandwich, a Couple of Olives and a Child's Cup full of Cocoa, while he wanted $35 worth of Ham and Eggs, a stack of Griddle Cakes and a Tureen of Coffee.

She was a case of Ambrosia and Nectar and he was plain old Ham and Spinach.

It used to give her Hysterics to see him bark at an Ear of Green Corn, at the same time making a Sound like a Dredge.

For Dinner she liked a little Consommé en Tasse and then a Nice Salad, while he insisted on a Steak the size of a Door Mat and German Fried to come along.

They did not Mocha and Java at all on their Reading Matter. She liked Henry James and Walter Pater and he preferred Horse Papers and the Comic Supplement. Sometimes when she would wander off into the Realms of Poesy he would follow her as far as he could, and then sit down and wait for her to get through rambling and come back.

If they took in a Show she was always plugging for Mrs. Fiske or Duse, while he claimed that Rogers Brothers were better than Booth and Barrett had been in their Prime.

She would weep over a Tosti Serenade, and he would walk a Mile at any time to see a good Buck Dance.

When they got around to fixing up Invitation Lists, there was more or less Geeing and Hawing.

All of his Friends belonged to the Hit-em-up Division. Their only Conception of a Happy Evening was to put the Buck in the Centre of the Table, break a fresh Pack and go out for Blood.

Wifey found her most delirious Joy in putting passionate Shades on all the Lamps, and sitting there in the Crimson Glow to discuss Maeterlinck and Maarten Maartens and a few others that were New Ones on the he-end of the Sketch.

When they had an Evening At Home up in the Flat, it was usually a two-ring Affair. She would have the Cerebellums in the Front Room looking at the New Books and eating Peppermint Wafers, while he and the other Comanches would be out in the Dining-Room trying to make their House Rent and tossing off that which made Scotland famous. Sometimes it would take half the Night to get the Smoke out of the House.

Although she feared that she had turned up the wrong Street while searching for her Affinity, the Partnership Arrangement had to stand.

They came to the Conclusion that Married Life is a Series of Compromises. If he did well while sitting in with some of his Friends, he would divide up with her and she would take the Money and buy Art Pastels.

He would spot the Afternoons on which the Ethical Researchers were due at his Premises and he would go to a Dutch Restaurant.

She permitted him to have a Room and call it his Den, so

that he and his Friends could do the Escape in case somebody in the Parlor started a Reading.

He put up the Coin to enable her to attend State Conventions, and when she was elected Recording Secretary of the Society for trying to find out what Browning was up to, he took her Picture around to all the Newspapers and told every one that he had a little Woman up at the House who was as Keen as a Hawk, as Swift as an Eagle, and Sharper than Chained Lightning.

He fumbled a great many of her In-Shoots, but that did not prevent him from admiring her Delivery.

Finally they arranged their separate Schedules so that they did not see much of each other and they began to get along all right. Occasionally they had a slight Difference, but they could always patch it up. For instance, she selected Aubrey De Courcey as a Name for the First Born, while he held out for Bill, so they had to compromise on Aubrey De Courcey.

Aubrey is now ten years of age. Mother is teaching him to Crochet and Father is showing him how to Draw without tipping off his Hand, while all the Friends are sitting around, waiting to see Aubrey's Finish.

Moral: *The Two of a Kind is not always the Strongest Combination.*

The Effort to Convert the Work Horse Into a High-Stepper

Once there was a plain, unvarnished Yank who made his Pile in a Scrub Town situated midway between the Oats Belt and the Tall Timber. He was a large and sandy Mortal with a steeltrap Jaw and a cold glittering Eye. He made his first Stack a Dollar at a Time on straight Deals, but after a while he learned a few Things. He organized Stock Companies and then crawled out after hooking up with the Velvet. Everyone called him Mister and treated him with Politeness, but, just the same, when he walked into an Office Building they all wondered what he had come after and there was more or less locking of Safes. It is only fair to remark, on the Side, that he wouldn't take anything which was securely spiked down, and the Grand Jury never bothered him, because he worked under a Contract.

The Financier was the high Centre Pole of a Bank and a Department Store and several Factories that gave Young People a Start in the World at something like $2.75 per Week.

He was accustomed to having all the Subordinates stand on one Foot and tremble whenever he showed up. In fact, he was a very hefty Proposition all through the Business District. But when he struck the Street leading to his House he began to reef his Sails and lower all of his Flags.

In his own Domicile he did not even play Second Fiddle. He simply trailed along at the fag end of the Parade and carried the Music. The Piercing Eye and the Peremptory Manner that caused all the Book-keepers to fall off from their High Perches and prostrate themselves had no visible effect on Laura and the Girls. Popsy was a High Guy at the Directors' Meeting, but a mighty cheap Soufflé at his own Fireside. Any time that his Plans did not coincide with those of the Feminine Bunch, they passed him a backhanded Veto that would cause him to lie quiet for Days at a time.

The Financier loved the boundless West, where the Sack Coat abounds and the Cuss-Word is a common Heritage. Domestic Cigars were good enough for him, and he figured that one good reliable Hired Girl who knew how to cook Steak was all the Help that was needed in any House. But Mother had seen Fifth Avenue in a Dream, and the Girls had attended a Boarding School at which nearly every one knew some one who was Prominent Socially. They had done a lot of Hard Work at the Piano and taken a sidehold on the French Language and it seemed to them that they were wasting their Time in loitering on the Outskirts of Civilization when they might be up at Headquarters cutting more or less of a Gash. All the Young Men in this Reub Town wore

Derbies with their Evening Clothes and came to Dances with their White Gloves smelling of Gasoline, in addition to which they lacked Repose. If they had stopped to cultivate Repose, most of them would have landed in the Villa set aside for Paupers.

When Laura and the Girls first advocated pulling up Stakes and doing a tall Hike to the East, the Producer emitted a Roar that would have frightened any one except Laura and the Girls. They closed in on him from three Directions and beat down his Defence. When they got through with the living Meal Ticket he was as meek as an English Servant and ready to take orders from any one.

So the Caravansary moved away toward the Rising Sun. At Wilkesbarre, Pennsylvania, the Heavens opened and a Great Light struck down upon them, transforming all except the one who happened to carry the Letter of Credit. Laura and the Girls suddenly forgot that there was any Land west of Pittsburgh, and they dropped their R's and got the Kangaroo Walk and began to order their Food in Foreign Languages. After that, all Father had to do was to follow along and look Pleasant and dig every few Minutes.

The Outfit stopped at the Waldorf three days so as to obtain a Residence, and after that they Registered as being from New York. Then they threw Papa on a Boat and took him to the Other Side, the Place where Americans are so Popular, if you don't care what you say. By paying off the Mortgage they obtained a Suite at a Hotel patronized by the Nobility and Gentry and supported by People from Iowa. After which they began to present Letters of Introduction and try to butt in. Laura and the Girls felt that if only they could eat a Meal once or twice in the gloomy Presence of those who had Handles to their Names, they would be ready to fall back and die Happy. They had some Trouble about getting into the Tall Game on account of their Money. In the States the general Run of People worship the Almighty Dollar, but in England they hate the Sight of it.

In spite of the Fact that they were sinfully Rich they succeeded in Elbowing their way into several Dinners at which it was necessary to put Ice into the Claret in order to keep it at the Temperature of the Room. The Financier, in his First Part Clothes with an Ice-Cream Weskit, was a Picture that no Artist could paint. His hair would not stay combed and he hardly ever knew what to do with his Hands.

Laura and the Girls could forget that they had once seen the Missouri River, but not so with Old Ready Money. Right at the Table, sitting opposite the Earl of Hammersmith or the Marquis of Stroke-on-Trent, while Laura and the Girls would be talking about their Country Place and trying to smother the American Accent, the Lobsterine would come in and tell about something that happened to him once when he was plowing Corn. Then Laura and the Girls would want to duck right under the Table and die of Mortification then and there.

The only Reason they put up with him was that he seemed to be useful when it came to signing Checks.

In England they met a great many Nice People. The Financier knew that they were Nice because they wore Dark Clothes and seldom Smiled.

Then the two shapely Daughters went and married a couple of shelf-worn Titles.

The Financier had the Novel Experience of putting up for a Brace of Sons-in-Law who would not speak to him when any one was around. Which served him right, for he had no Business to be in Trade. It was very careless of him not to have inherited his Stuff.

Still, it was a great Satisfaction to him to be a Blood Relative of two Howling Swells who had Pedigrees reaching back almost as far as their Debts.

Very often he would take them into a Back Room and turn them around and look them over and recognize the cold, undeniable Fact that they were cheap at any Price.

Moral: *Bunker Hill has been Avenged, over and over.*

Self-Made Hezekiah and His Message of Hope to This Year's Crop of Graduates

In Wayback Township, along in the Thirties, there arrived a 12-pounder. When he was three days old he was exhibited to a Bunch in the Front Room by an Old Lady who had made a Study of Colic. She was a Baby Expert who always broke in to do considerable heavy standing around and calling off when there was a lift in the Population.

While little Ipsy-Wipsy was being inspected, he opened one Eye and spotted a silver Half-Dollar that the Honorary Nurse wore as a Brooch. Immediately he closed in on it. They had to choke him to make him let go. In after Years it was remarked that this was the only time that he went after the Coin and failed to bring it home.

The Baby never had any Tantrums at Night because he had overheard them say that it cost $2 every time Doc was called in. He would lie quietly in his Crib for Hours at a time looking up at the Ceiling and computing Compound Interest on the $5 Gold Piece that had been put in the Bank, to be drawn out when he should be 21.

His Parents gave him a Biblical Name so as to make him a strong Come-On for Investors who belong to the Pious Element. Hezekiah Hooper is what they christened him. They wanted a Name that would carry weight on a Letter-Head and reassure the Soft Mark who was about to sink his Funds in a Mining Venture with a Guarantee of 48 per cent. Dividends.

At the age of 4 Hezekiah sat down and figured that if he devoted his Life to Physical Toil, he might some day be the Owner of a six-room cottage fully protected by a Mortgage, whereas if he wore a White Shirt and kept busy with the Pencil, he might be Rich enough some day to land in the Senate. So he went out looking for Work to hand to other People, thus becoming what the Campaign Orator calls a Captain of Industry.

If a man wanted the Weeds pulled from his Garden, then

Hez would take the Job for 25 cents. He would buy 5 cents worth of Stick Candy and place it judiciously, so that at Nightfall the other boys would have Blisters and the Stomach-Ache, while Hez would have 20 cents salted away in the Tin Bank.

When he was still a Young Man he made the Important Discovery that the honest Laborer who digs Post-Holes for 11 Hours at a Stretch gets $1.25 in the Currency of the Realm, while the Brain-Worker who leads out a Spavined Horse and puts in 20 Minutes at tall Bunko Work, can clean up $14.50 and then sit on the Porch all Afternoon, reading "The Lives of the Saints."

Also Hezekiah led up to the Altar a Hold-Over whose Eyes refused to work as a Duet and whose Figure had all of the graceful Ins and Outs of a Flag-Pole, but she owned half of the Land in the Township. Hezekiah said something about the Beauty that fadeth even as a Flower, and then he connected with her Property.

When Grim-visaged War showed its awful Front, Hezekiah went down to the Court-House and hollered for the Union until he was black in the Face. He showed all the emotional Farm Hands where to sign their Names and promised to keep them supplied with Blue Overcoats, Beans, Navy Plug and Hard Tack until the whole Works had been saved. Every time there was a new Call for Men, he took a firmer hold on the Commissary Department and began to gouge the Government in a new Place.

The Heroes who came home full of Malaria and Lead were met at the Station by Hezekiah, who had grown a Chin Whisker and was sporting a White Vest. He gave each one a Card announcing that all of our country's Brave Defenders who had failed to become well fixed on $3 per, would get what Money they needed at 2 per cent. a Month, with Real Estate as Security.

By going through Bankruptcy, side-stepping the Assessor, working the Farmers for a Railroad Bonus, handling the Funds for denominational Colleges and putting the double

Hammer-Lock on the Small Fry who had Notes falling due, Hezekiah accumulated a Wad that put him into the Millionaire's Division.

He and other old Gentlemen with pink Jowls and cold Fishy Eyes would occasionally meet in some Directors' Room, finished in Mahogany. The Meeting would be opened with Prayer, after which they would discuss Ways and Means of putting the Inter-State Commerce Law to the Bad, squaring the Legislature without passing over any of the Stuff themselves and handing the Public the Short End of it.

Having arrived at this Proud Eminence, Hezekiah was ripe to spring some Advice to Young Men. Any Patriarch who has slipped the Tall Mitt to the entire Universe and dealt from both Ends of the Deck is the Real Boy when it comes to laying down Rules of Conduct for the Pale Youth who wants an $8 Job. So Hezekiah Hooper, the Eminent Financier, who never smoked a Cigar, never took a Drink and never asked anybody else to do either, was invited to address the Class of Naughty-Three at the Local Business College.

He sat on the Rostrum wearing Black Broadcloth, betokening Virtue, and in addition to his ancient Trade-Marks, the White Shirt and the White Vest, he had a White Bow Tie. As he sat there in conscious Rectitude, wondering if the Congressional Investigation would harm the Beef Trust, it could be seen at a Glance that he would never take anything that was too heavy to carry, unless he had a Dray.

The studious Young Gentlemen who had been preparing themselves to go out into the Great World and draw Car-Fare as Book-Keepers, and Stenographers, looked up at Honest Hezekiah and said, "This is where he puts us next to the Recipe for Getting There."

At last the Honored Guest arose and told the Class that the Young Man who wishes to succeed must be Upright, Frugal, Industrious, and Patriotic. He considered it the Duty of every Young Man to accept whatever Compensation was offered him and be Content, for as soon as he began to earn more his Employer would come around and put it in his Pocket. Above all, he must love his Country and let Integrity be his Watchword and remember that a Good Name is better than Riches, even if other People don't think so. Then he sat down without batting an Eye and every member of the Class of '03 knew just how to go out and pile up a Million.

Moral: *What's more, they believe it themselves.*

The Girl Who Took Notes and Got Wise and Then Fell Down

Once upon a Time there was a long-headed Girl who used to sit in her own Room on Rainy Afternoons and evolve Theories. Her principal Ambition in Life was to stand Ace High with all the Nice Men of her Set. She hoped in the course of Time to tease one away from the Drove and gallop him into the Branding Pen.

Now this Girl was so Foxy that at times she got in front of herself and blocked off her own Plays. Her scheme for getting all the Real Boys intoxified with Love for her was to engage them in Conversation and find out what kind of Girls they liked. Then her Play was to be that Kind. She had no Difficulty whatever in inducing her Men Friends to talk about the Opposite Sex. They were all keyed up on the Subject and full of Information. Just as a Feeler one Evening she asked an eligible Charley if he didn't think that the Woman of To-day was too Extravagant.

"That's just why so many of us shy at the Matrimonial Jump," he confided to her. "There was a time when the Man who got $75 per Month and had about $200 planted could take a Chance at the Game. But now that measly Allowance wouldn't keep a High Roller supplied with Violets. The up-to-date Maudine isn't happy unless she has a Gray-Squirrel Coat, an Auto Car, $11,000 worth of Twinklers and a fourteen-room Apartment. That's why these Society Shawl-

Holders keep on making Love right and left but never come down to Cases."

This was a valuable Tip, so the crafty Maiden put it down in her little Note-Book that she who would make a Hit must convince the Men that her Tastes were simple and inexpensive. Another one gave her a learned Talk on the frivolity and Two-by-Fourness of the typical Seraphine.

"You cannot expect a Man to hand over his serious Affections to one of these Feather-Heads," he said, as he gazed thoughtfully at the Floor. "Woman should be Man's Intellectual Helpmeet. Now and then a Man may have a Passing Fancy for a Lizzie who talks Piffle and gets an Attack of the Giggles every few Seconds, but when it comes to the grand Hook-up he wants one who is there with the Gray Matter—one who can play up to his loftiest Ambitions and supply his Home with that Atmosphere of Culture which is the true Ozone of Married Life."

So she put it down that it was her Cue to chop out the Twaddle and be a sort of Lady Emerson. Incidentally she resolved to cut out all kinds of Slang, for she got a very straight Line of Talk from an Amateur Philosopher who was in the Wholesale Grocery Business.

"If there's anything that gives me a quick, shooting Pain it is to hear some delicate Nectarine dealing out Slang," said Mr. Gentleman Friend. "Now in England, where I spent Two Weeks once, the Ladies never use Slang. They simply say that a Thing is either Perfectly Charming or Most Estraordinary and let it got at that. They may be Short on Vocabulary, but they are Long on Respectability. Besides, I was reading in a Magazine the other Day that Slang is Vulgar and that no one should take up with a Slang Word until Long Usage has given it the right to break into the Lexicon."

This Girl with the Absorbent Mind would clip out Hints to the Young, and Confidential Charts warning the Just-Outs against taking Presents from Strangers and putting them next to Rules of Conduct that would be sure to please and fascinate Proper Young Men. It seemed strange at Times that these Head Coaches who knew just how to jolly up any Man were not out spending some Millionaire's Money instead of writing Pieces for the Paper.

All the Articles on the Woman's Page and all the strait-laced Men that she met came down Hard on the Female who is trying to be a Real Bohemian. She learned from a dozen different Sources that Men have no earthly Use for the Zipper who tries to do a Mile in less than Two and kites around in a Hack without a Chaperon and carries her own Cigarettes.

And she heard nothing but Expressions of Horror concerning the Woman who Drinks. Her Male acquaintances often brought up the Painful Subject. They said it was all right for a Man to move up to a High Ball once in a While, and a Cocktail before Dinner didn't do any Harm until after the Seventh or Eighth. But it did look Tough to see Mere Children of about twenty-three Years of Age going after the Dry Manhattans.

After sounding the Men on the Liquor Question the long-headed Girl made a solemn Resolve that she would never hit up anything stronger than Cherry Sundae.

When she had her Note Book full of useful Directions she found a Chance to try out her System. She was invited to a Swell Dinner Party at which all the Nice Men in Town were to be rounded up. She put on a simple White Gown and wore a Rose in her Hair, and just before starting she locked all of her Slang words in the Escritoire, whatever that may be.

At the Dinner she sat next to a Bachelor who had Nothing But. She talked to him about the Panama Canal, just to show that she was no Piker. When he wanted her to take some of the Phizz Water she made an Awful Stand and seemed surprised that he should think that of her.

This did not prevent him from splashing in. By the time the Birds came along he had accumulated a very neat Brannigan, and was paying a lot of Attention to a wonderful Piece of Work sitting opposite. She wore a Red Costume that must have cost $7,000, and although she was very gabby and called the Men by their First Names and invited all who were not Quitters to stand by for a Bumper, she was making fair Headway. In fact, she seemed to have the Bunch with her.

The Wise Girl figured that they were tolerating her out of mere Politeness. Later on, in the Drawing Room, they continued to tolerate her the best they knew how. The Girl with the Book of Rules played a sad little Opus on the Piano, after which the Steeple-Chaser in Red leaped on top of the Instrument and tore out Coon Stuff with eight men turning the Music for her.

And these were the Eight who had told the Girl back in the Corner all about the Qualities in Woman that would help to attract Men. She went home thinking it over and the next time she started for a Dinner, she added a Dash of Red and a few Brilliants to the Costume and cut loose up to a reasonable Limit. She got along first-rate, even though she was doing a lot of Things that none of the Men approve, but somehow love to put up with.

Moral: *He can always pick out the Right Kind for the Other Fellow.*

The Fable of the Divided Concern that Was Reunited Under a New Management

Once upon a Time there was a Firm doing Business under the Name of Hailfellow and Grouch.

They had a large Retail Establishment, upon entering which the Customer was greeted by the mingled Odors of Kerosene, Roasted Coffee, Leather, Herkimer County Cheese, Navy Plug, Dried Apples, and petrified Codfish. In the good old Summer-Time it was not necessary to go into the Store in order to get the complicated Aroma. Farmers driving by could come very near guessing what Hailfellow and Grouch carried in Stock.

The Firm did a Nice Business and used to split quite a Piece of Money every January 1st. But neither one was satisfied. Each felt that he was entitled to at least two-thirds of the Net Profits.

Mr. Hailfellow was he Hand-Shaker for the Outfit. His Long Suit was to know everybody and call him by his front Name. On every pleasant Day he stood in front of the fragrant Emporium, in his Shirt Sleeves, holding a public Levee.

He was a quiet Josher and knew a lot of good Jokes that he had once heard in a Minstrel Show at Columbus, Ohio, and that made him very strong with the Country Trade.

Furthermore, he was a good Mixer. He belonged to the K. P.'s and the Odd Fellows and a few others, so that about four Nights out of the week he would fill his Pockets with mild Smokers, usually neglecting to make out a Ticket, and then he would pike for the Lodge-Room and let his Partner and the Boy with the Pink Shirt attend to the Store.

If there was an Auction Sale or a Baseball Game or a Circus anywhere within a Radius of twenty Miles, then Mr. Hailfellow would put on his Dark Suit and stand-up Collar and drive over, just to get his Mind off his Business. In one Way and another he managed to keep his Mind off of Business about seven-eighths of the Time.

Sometimes, when he was around the Store, and there was a Saturday Rush, he would have to wait on a few Customers, but he was a shine Salesman because he never could make out what the Cost-Mark meant.

Mr. Grouch, the Partner, possessed a Good Head for Business, but he had the Social Disposition of a Coffin-Trimmer. While Hailfellow would be up and down the Street, kidding the local Population and making himself well liked, Grouch would be in the back end of the Store straightening out the Books and figuring Discounts.

Grouch was at the Store by 7 o'clock every Morning, keeping Tab, for fear that some one who was No Good would get his Name on the Books.

Hailfellow would land in about 9.30 and open the Day by

reading the Morning Paper through from the Weather Bulletin in front to the Testimonials on the last Page. After which he was ready to go out and plant himself on a Salt-Barrel and discuss the Issues of the Day.

Grouch had only one Day off in Four Years, and then he had to attend the Funeral of a Relative. So that when he did get a Vacation there was not much Enjoyment in it.

There was no denying his Industry, but no one liked him. He seemed to have some kind of an inward Grudge against every one who came in to buy a Bill of Goods. If a Customer remarked that it was a Nice Day, he didn't seem to believe it. The Trade would not have stuck at all, had it not been for Hailfellow, who had a way of giving Stick Candy to the Kids and beautiful Colored Pictures, advertising Breakfast Foods, to the Women Folks.

Each Partner naturally believed that he was getting the Short End of the Arrangement. They would go home and tell their Troubles to the Wives. Mrs. Hailfellow went around to Sewing Societies and Missionary Meetings telling how Mr. Hailfellow had to put up with a lot and was really the one who brought all the Trade to the Store.

Mrs. Grouch loved to let all her Friends know that her Husband slaved like a Dog while the Partner soldiered, but, just the same, always came in on the cut-up of the Profits.

When the Wives begin to take part in a Business Row, the Dissolution Notice is about Due.

Hailfellow and Grouch agreed to disagree. Hailfellow took his Share and opened a New Place across the Street, with a Gilt Sign and nickel-plated Show-Cases.

Almost immediately it was the most popular Joint in Town. At Times there were as many as ten Men sitting around the Stove swapping Fish Stories. Hailfellow employed a couple of Clerks who knew more about a Cash Register than the Man that invented it.

He issued Pass-Books to all those who cared for his Jokes. The Drummers would jump several Towns in order to get to him in a Hurry, because, if Hailfellow liked a Drummer, he would order a thousand gross of Lamp Chimneys rather than appear cold and unsociable. In a short time he had a Magnificent Stock, but he could not remember exactly how much it cost him. So he sold Goods at whatever seemed to be Reasonable and the Farmers drove long distances so as to give him their Trade.

In the meantime Grouch was reaping the sure Reward of one who is not kind to his Fellow-Man. People did not care to patronize one whose Conversation consisted very largely of Grunts, and why should they do so when they could go right across the Street and buy Stuff below Cost, and a Joke given away with every Purchase?

Grouch began to lose Money and the Rent ate up his Invested Capital. At last the Jobbers closed in on him and asked the Sheriff to step in, and the Sheriff said he would do so as soon as he got through closing up the Hailfellow Matter.

Mr. Hailfellow had done a rushing Business. He owed nearly every Wholesale House west of New York, and in addition to laying up the most remarkable mess of Junk ever seen under one Roof, he had collected the Autograph Signatures of all the Paupers in the County. Four Experts worked for a Month trying to find out where he stood, and at last they figured out Fourteen Cents on the Dollar.

It is always pleasant to record a Reconciliation. After all their Differences and Misunderstandings, Hailfellow and Grouch came together and resumed Friendly Relations.

Both are employed by a New Concern which bought up the Bankrupt Stocks.

Grouch is keeping the Books at not very much per Month, and Hailfellow receives exactly the same Salary for standing around the front Doorway and glad-handing the Yaps.

Which proves that it is impossible for a Business Man to side-step his Destiny.

Moral: *Pick out the Other Kind for a Partner.*

The Fable of Successful Tobias and Some of His Happy New-Years

Once there was a Financial Heavy-Weight, the Mile-Stones of whose busy Life were strung back across the Valley of Tribulation into the Green Fields of Childhood.

Like most of our Aristocrats, he got his Start out among the Corn-Rows.

His Youth was spent very happily, but he did not get on to the Fact until Years later. He used to work Fourteen Hours per for his Board and Clothes, and his only Dissipation was to take in the Swiss Bell-Ringers once every Season.

At the Close of every Year he was permitted to attend a Watch-Meeting at the Mt. Zion Church. The Watch-Meeting is a form of Gayety invented a long time ago by some one who was not feeling well at the Time.

The Outfit were supposed to sit for three or four Hours on the hard Benches, meditating on all the low-down, ornery Things they had done during the Old Year. Some of them had to hurry in order to crowd this Line of Meditation into a brief four Hours.

Now and then a local High-Guy with Throat Whiskers would arise and talk for a short time on the Subject of Death, and wonder how many of those present would be taken in by the Grim Reaper during the New Year.

Just at Midnight the Sexton would toll the Bell so as to cheer every one up. Then each of the Merry-Makers would go home and eat a Piece of Mince Pie and a Belle Flower Apple and retreat to the Feathers, feeling a little Ashamed for having stayed up so Late.

Later on, after Tobias moved into Town and began to wear Store Clothes and Stand-Up Collars and put Oil on his Hair, he encountered another kind of New-Year's Day.

The Era was that of the Open House. All the Women received, and the Men went over the entire Circuit and traded job-printed Cards for something to Eat and Drink.

This made it Fine for those who were not ordinarily invited into the Best Homes.

The Men roamed about in Flocks and usually they had a Hard Finish, for it was customary in those good old Days of Democratic Simplicity for every True Gentleman to take a Drink when it was proffered by the Hand of Lovely Woman.

And Lovely Woman seemed to regard it as her Assignment to put all of the Nice Young Fellows to the Bad.

It was customary to mix Tea, Coffee, Sherbet, Lemonade, Egg-Nog, Artillery Punch, Fizzerine, and Straight Goods until the Happy New-Year looked like a scrambled Rainbow and the last Caller was Sozzled.

Tobe used to go out every New-Year's Day to meet the Good-Lookers and fuss around with them, for those were his Salad Days. He made it a Combination Salad and philandered with about Seven before he took the Big Risk and bought a Home with a Mortgage Attachment and settled down.

Then the Happy New-Year began to have an entirely new Meaning.

He drew a Red Mark around January 1st, for that was the Day when he had to make the Books balance and take up some big Note that was hanging over him like a Storm Cloud.

His usual Plan for celebrating the Happy New-Year was to sit in his Office figuring on how to trim the Pay-Roll and sneak up Selling Prices and keep out of the Sheriff's Hands for another Twelve Months.

But the Time came when Tobias could take out a Pencil on December 31st and compute a Net Profit big enough to fill a Furniture Van.

To all Intents and Purposes he had come to the High Ground where he could afford to sit down for a while and enjoy the Scenery.

He certainly possessed all the Accessories of a Happy New-Year.

He had a Bank Roll and a House on the Boulevard and a

Wife who was slowly but surely worming her Way into Society.

He had a Son attending a high-priced University and gradually accumulating an Oxford Accent, while his Daughter was at a School which used the French Novel as a Text-Book.

So, after all these Years of Struggling, Tobias knew what it was to have a genuinely Happy New-Year.

For when the Children came Home for the Holiday Vacation the busy Mrs. Tobias gave a big Dancing Party on New-year's Eve, to say nothing of a couple of Luncheons and a Formal Dinner.

At these glittering Functions the Family did what it could to keep Tobias in the Background, for while he was a Corker when it came to doing a Fountain-Pen Specialty with a Check-Book, he was a Frosted Turnip when chucked into a Suit costing $100 and put down in a Marie Antoinette Apartment with a lot of Chaunceys who had been educated in the East.

He celebrated the Glad New-Year by standing around in Doorways and looking mournfully at the Light-Weights who were doing the Cotillion, and each of them having the Time of his Life.

He saw his Wife hob-nobbing with a Human Pickerel whose only Excuse for being on Earth was that he looked well in Evening Clothes.

Daughter was dancing with a lovely Specimen of the night-blooming Rounder, and Son was passing Cigarettes. And no one was paying any Attention to the Provider.

So he made a quiet Retreat to his own Room and had a Glass of Milk sent up, and read the Market Report, and managed to put in a Pleasant Evening, after all, seeing the Old One out and the New One in.

Moral: *One New Year is just about as Happy as another.*

The Fable of the Red-Letter Night at Smartweed Junction

Once there was an under-sized Town that had the Corn-Fields sneaking up on all sides of it, trying to break over the Corporation Line. People approaching the Town from the North could not see it, because there was a Row of Willow-Trees in the Way.

Here in this comatose Settlement lived a Family named Pilkins. The Pilkinses were all the Eggs in Smartweed. They owned a big General Store catty-cornered from the Court-House. It was well known that they sent to Chicago for their Clothes and ate Ice-Cream in the Winter-Time. The Pilkins Girls had been away to a Convent to have their Voices sandpapered and fitted to a Piano and they came back with the first Gibson Shirt-Waists seen in those Parts. Most of the Girls south of the Tracks were just getting wise to the Russian Blouse.

Along in May the Pilkins Family made its annual Play to set the Prairies on fire. Every Adult in Town, except those who had Jail Records, received an Engraved Invitation to come up to the Pilkins House and take a peek at High Life. Within three Days you couldn't buy a Yard of Wide Ribbon in any Store and every Second Man in Mink Patterson's Barber Shop asked for a Hair-Cut. The R.S.V.P. down in one Corner of the Bid had some of the Brethren guessing for a while. There was no need of putting that on. It was an immortal Cinch that every one would turn out, if he had to be moved in on a Cot. About the only Entertainments they had in Smartweed Junction were "Uncle Tom" under a Tent and the Indian Medicine Troupe. Therefore, nobody was going to pass up the Pilkins Jamboree, for there was to be an imported Orchestra, costing $75, and Meals provided, and the City Caterer was to bring his own Waiters.

Everybody went home early that Day so as to take a good thorough Scouring before getting into his Other Clothes. At Dusk they began wending their Way towards the Pilkins

Place, all looking a little worried and apprehensive. They were sorted out at the Front Door and led into Dressing-Rooms, pegged out along the Walls, fed on Macaroons, and treated to large Bunches of Bach Music. Every half-hour or so somebody would say something, and that would be a Cue for the others to shift their Feet.

The Punch-Bowl got the Cold Eye until it was learned that the Dyestuff was Aniline and not Rum, and then they stood around and dipped in until they were blue under the Ears.

About 11 o'clock the Japanese Lanterns began to burn up and a large number of People whose Feet were hurting them could be seen quietly Ducking. The Home Paper said it was the Event of the Season.

Moral: *Eat, Drink, and be Merry, for To-morrow ye Die.*

The Fable of What Horace Stood For in Order to Land the Queen

Once there was a Lover who was on the Ragged Edge of the Desert where the Old Bachelors live.

He was good and tired of the Aristocratic Boarding-House, in which one-half of the Women Folks are Private Detectives. This thing of living in a Pigeon-Hole and looking out at a Tin Roof had lost all Rarity and Charm for Horace.

He had gazed into the barren Future and made up his mind to Marry, even if he had to choke some Nice Girl in order to force her to say "Yes." He was all keyed up for Matrimony, and the next thing to do was to choose the Lucky Bride.

Horace had done more or less rehearsing and he was wise to the Fact that it is just as easy to love a Girl who has the Coin as it is to get dippy over the Honest Working-Girl. Some Men imagine that the Foxy Play is to grab off something that never owned any Sunbursts and Sable Wraps, and probably she will be satisfied with Department-Store Belt Buckles and Nearsilk Trimmings.

But Horace observed that those who never had been strong enough to throw on the Lugs while they were living at Home, were the very ones who put Crimps into the Bank Account before the Honeymoon played out.

Horace often suspected that some of them hooked up merely to get a Whack at the Finery. But then, Horace was a regular old Cynic.

So he decided that he would pick one whose Folks had already bought for her about everything she would need.

After travelling the Beat for a Month and putting down Names in his Pocket Memorandum-Book, he drew a Red Mark around the Name of Lucille, and the same Day he sent her some Orchids and a New Book that he knew she would Enjoy, because it had such a Sweet Love-Story running through it.

Soon after that the Girl at Central began to know all about the Progress of the Affair. Lucille was all around the Neighborhood assuring People that, although Horace had been lovely to her and she esteemed him as one of her dearest and kindest Friends, there was really and truly nothing doing. Consequently, every one could see how it was going to turn out.

Horace had fondly supposed that the Recipe for becoming engaged was simply to warm up to the Girl until he could Hold Hands without using Brute Force, and then wait for the Psychological Moment. So one Night when Lucille looked up into his Eyes and said he was different from any other Gentleman she had ever met, he came back with the Speech. Her only Reply was to slip him one of Papa's Business Cards which she had ready for the Occasion.

"Go and square yourself with him," said Lucille.

Next Morning, Horace, wearing his best Bib and Tucker (also 8,000,000 Goose Pimples), was shown into Papa's Office. First he had to tell all about his Assets and his Business Experience, but that didn't take long. Then he told how much he saved every month. If he swelled it a little, it was because he loved the Girl.

After he had answered all the Questions, he had to sit and listen to that well-known Monologue which is the Prize Specialty of the Self-Made Party who began Life by working for Seven Dollars per Month and saving Five Dollars of it. Lucille's Father said that Young Men nowadays are too extravagant and not half as Industrious and Keen as he had been about the Time that he escaped from the Farm. He sat there and hurled Bouquets at himself until his Arm gave out, after which he told Horace to go and fix it with Lucille's Mother.

Mother wanted to know, first, if he was willing to be married in the Episcopalian Church. He had to tell all about his Family. She seemed much relieved when she learned that he had Relatives in Virginia. Horace knew that part of it would be all right—unless she should happen to see the Relatives some Day.

She told him why a House was preferable to a Flat and scratched two or three of his Suggestions for Ushers. After letting him know that he would cut but little Ice at the Ceremony, she suggested that he go over and make himself solid with Uncle Samuel, because he had been accustomed to hold Lucille on his Knee when she was a mere Tot.

And, of course, that gave him a right to butt in on all Family Issues.

Uncle Samuel asked Horace what Church he attended regularly. The only thing that saved Horace was that he happened to remember the Name of a Church. Horace tried to side-step the Questions about Drinking and Smoking, but Uncle pinned him down, so he said that he had been tempted but he had not fallen, as yet.

After running the Family Gauntlet, Horace heaved a Sigh of Relief and believed that he had clinched all the Preliminaries. Not so. He had forgotten to fix it up with his own Firm.

An Employé can go on the outside and do almost anything and the Firm will not interfere, but the Minute he talks Marry, then old Mr. Side-Whiskers sends for him to come to the Private Office. The reason for this is that every Antique in the Wholesale District has a lot of cut-and-dried Advice which he loves to unload on any one who is compelled to stand and take it. So Horace learned from his respected Boss that for two or three Years the Couple should live on Cereal Food and make their own Clothes.

The next Bunch of Warning and Advice came from the True Friends at the Club. They put him down at a Table and sat around him and inhaled the Scotch until they were all Pie-Eyed, and then they told him what a Horrible Risk he was taking, and how not more than a half-dozen Married Men in town seemed really happy, and, although she was a Nice Girl, she had been engaged two or three times before, and Mother-in-Law would be a fierce Proposition.

For a Hammer Duet, the Men's Club makes the Boiler-Works seem like the Hush of Death.

The Reader may suspect that Horace was actuated by Mercenary Motives. However, the fact that he went the Rounds and listened to every one and then married the Girl proves that he truly loved her.

Moral: *Elope.*

The Fable of the Boy with the Steadfast Ambition

In a Small Place where the Local Freight stopped to rake out the Ashes and pick up a Car of Produce, there was a Boy who had set his Heart on being a Railroad Man. He would go down to the Depot and look at the Head Brakeman on No. 4, and say to himself: "Some Day I shall be like him if I improve my Opportunities and learn to make a Coupling on the Run without the use of a Stick."

He was down flipping the Trains every day, in defiance of the Town Marshal, and he wore a flat-topped Hat, and Braid on his Clothes, and chewed Conductor's Delight. All that he needed to be a real Railroader was a large Silver Watch and a few Orders written on yellow Tissue-Paper.

It was a Proud Day when they put him on an Extra Run, for then he was privileged to speak of the Superintendent as the Old Man and wave his hand at all the Dining-Room Girls along the Line.

Just as he was becoming well acquainted with all the Agents and Operators and had acquired a large Vocabulary to be used in cussing the Engineer, he got what seems to be due every Brakeman. He was a little slow in withdrawing the Left Fin and the Bumpers caught him. When he came out of the Hospital his Left Hand looked like a Pair of Scissors. Then he was a sure-enough Railroader. He went back on the Road, and the next time they landed him Right. He got mixed up in a head-on Collision and a Gravel Train piled up on top of him. By the time the Surgeons had pared away what wouldn't be any more use to him he was trimmed down to about three-quarters Size. As soon as he got his Crutches he went back and got a Job on a Crossing, where his Duties were to wave a Red Flag and criticise the Policy of the Road. One Day his Uncle, a well-to-do Citizen, came along and said to what was left of him: "If you had taken my Advice, you would be a successful Business Man with the usual number of Arms and Legs."

Then the Remnant replied as follows:

"When the Choo-Choo Microbe begins to work on a Man, he would rather be a crippled Brakeman than an athletic Bank President."

Moral: *He whose Soul is in Railroading never objects to being Marked Up a little.*

The Fable of the Unfortunate Has-Been and the Sympathetic Conductor

In an open-faced Car sat a glib Person and a decrepit Old Gentleman with a haggard and sorrowful Frontispiece.

The two dropped into a Conversation and soon began opening up their Private Affairs, according to the Western Fashion. The glib Party told how much he was drawing and how he invested it, and all about several gigantic Schemes that he had under his Cuff. The Antique with the pall-bearing Face did not enthuse.

"Young Man, you will learn that Life is a series of wasted Opportunities and vain Regrets," he said. "When you are all in and a new Generation comes along and gives you a good swift Bump and you light on your Back over by the Fence, then you can lie there and look up at the Sky and count the Good Things that got past you."

With that the broken-hearted Patriarch sprang a lovely Bundle of Hard-Luck Tales. He pointed out a Corner Lot, now valued at a Half-Million, that had been offered to him for $350. Once he had been given a Chance to trade a second-hand Buggy for a half-interest in a Patent that netted a couple of Thousand each Day. The Stock in the Street Railway Company he closed out at seven. Afterward it went to 293.

"I used to own the Ground where the First National stands," he said, with Tears in his Eyes. "Like a blithering Pin-Head, I traded it for a Team of Mules. If I hadn't been all kinds of a Ninny, I could have got in on the Ground Floor of the Standard Oil. And now I'm getting too old and weak to kick myself."

At the next Corner the ancient Wreck alighted and tottered on his Way.

"Is it not a Sad Case?" said the Young Man to the Conductor. "How bitter must be his reflections when he counts up what he might have nailed if he had been Foxy."

"Yes, I feel sorry for him," said the Humane Conductor,

who was drawing Eight Dollars per Week. "All he can show is a measly Two Millions. What breaks his Heart is that he doesn't own both sides of the Street and the Green Cars that run in between."

Moral: *The Kicker is the Man who gets Part of it.*

The Fable of How Gertrude Could Keep it Up until Ten O'Clock in the Morning

Gertrude had a Pa who wanted to know.

"It's all right to have your Harolds around the House," he said, "but why do you sit up half the Night every time one of them calls?"

"It is the Custom and it keeps him away from the Bar-Rooms," she replied.

"You may be doing it from a Sense of Duty, but you will have to show me," said her Father. "What in the Name of all Get-Out do you find to talk about? That one that's been around here lately could tell all he knows in twenty-five Minutes. Any time that he fills in from eight o'clock to Midnight he certainly has to do some Vamping."

"I assure you that he is a swell Converser," said Gertrude. "I could sit and listen to him by the Hour."

"If ever I set and listen to him by the Hour, it will be to win a large Bet," said her Parent.

That Night the inquisitive Father got behind a Curtain and listened. Harold had a Half-Nelson on Gertie and was trying to make it appear that he thought well of her.

"I don't believe you like me," said Gertrude.

"Oh yes, I do," quoth Harold.

"No, you don't."

"Yes, I do."

"No, you don't."

"Yes, I do."

On the seventy-second "Yes, I do" there was a Shriek and Gertrude's Pa came through the Curtains, having a Fit.

Moral: *Any kind of Conversation goes in a Clinch.*

The Fable of How the Fearless Favorite from St.Louis Flagged the Hot-Looker Across the Way

Once there was a Salesman who handled dried Fruits and registered from Saint Louey. He could tell about the Big Bridge and the Union Station and had a fifteen-minute Spiel touching on and appertaining to Desiccated Apples that was calculated to land the cross-roads Wanamaker.

Clarence, for such was his Name, had the Fatal Gift of Beauty and he was Wise to the Fact. He hated to turn out the Light at Night and have all his Good Looks go to waste for Hours at a Stretch.

What Nature had failed to do for him he did for himself. He kept his Neck neatly shaved and put Heliotrope on his Eyebrows and drank Florida Water to kill his Cigarette Breath before dashing into Society.

When Clarence had polished up his Rings and Stud with a Piece of Chamois and got into his Sack-Suit with the up-and-down Stripe and put on his nobby white Hat with the black Band, you may think that he despised himself, but he did not. It was like breaking Home Ties for him to say goodbye to a Mirror.

Clarence was not entirely to blame for being so Popular with himself. A good many of the swellest Dining-Room Girls on the Short Line between Herodsberg and Vandalia had fought for the Privilege of bringing him his Ribs of Beef with Brown Potatoes.

Whenever he unpacked at a Hotel he put a Photograph of Himself out on the Dresser, so as to make the Room more cheerful.

One Day it befell that Clarence, the Woman-Catcher, was riding in a Day Coach, and having a great deal of Trouble with his Cuffs because they would not stay out the right Length. Now and then he looked out of the Window, so as to give the Ladies behind a chance at his Profile.

At one of the Stations something tailor-made with more than the usual number of Eyes and the Style of a Frohman Leading Lady blew into the Car and seated herself opposite fascinating Clarence. He immediately tossed one Arm over the Back of the Seat so that she could get a Flash at the four-ounce Ring with the three Rock-Crystals in it. Also he began to do a Series of Living Pictures, at the same time sizing her carefully. She was about the gowniest he had seen since pulling out of Sedalia, and he decided that it was up to him to get acquainted.

He knew that he was taking a Chance, but an ordinary Toss had no Terrors for one accustomed to grappling with the Country Trade. So he took from his Grip a Copy of *Widow in Name Only,* by Ethel Gilblitz, author of *Lingering Love,* and the first thing she knew he was asking her if she wanted something to read.

Instead of trying to jump out of the Window, she received him with a glad Smile and moved over so as to make Room. At that Moment he realized that a Handsome Boy with Nerve can butt in at any time or place.

In low musical Notes, something like the Bird-Calls of the Forest, he told her about the House and the Bill of Goods he had sold in the last Town, and how he attented Progressive Cinch Parties every time he got back to Saint Louey. She listened with keen Interest and looked him right in the Eye, and never once did she call for Help.

It appeared to be the strongest Ten-Strike of his glorious Career as a Depot Flirt.

She wanted to know all about him, even to the Extent of sounding him on Literature and the Arts.

He told her that Dan McAvoy had Julia Marlowe beat at

least a Block when it come to putting up a Lively Show, and as for Books, he couldn't see Lew Wallace with a Spy-Glass, but the Duchess was Warm Stuff.

His Views carried so much Weight that she began to take Notes in a little Book. She asked him how much he made in Commissions and Salary, and what amount he spent on Clothes and Finery as compared with his Outlay for Soul-Food. He began to wing a little and realized that he was up against a New Game; but he could not renig after making the first Play, so she Pumped him properly.

Finally she asked him for a Photograph, which she numbered thirty-two and filed away in a Blue Envelope.

After which she said that would be about all, and some invisible Force seemed to lift him back to the other side of the Car. As he sat there, slowly recovering, it occurred to him that he had neglected to get her Name and Address and make her promise to Correspond, which was very careless of him. He thought some of making another Try, but she was busy with a Book, other than the one he had given to her, and seemed to have forgotten that he was right there in the same car.

Clarence began to suspect that he had failed to Entertain her, but such was not the case.

He did not see her again, but next Month his Friends called his Attention to an Article in an Eastern Periodical, written by a Lady who had been investigating the Intellectual Awakening of the Middle West. She gave Clarence quite a Send-off and used his Picture, calling attention to the lack of Forehead and the Vacant Expression about the Eyes. She said he was a Type of the Middle-Class Materialist, who cared more for Personal Adornment than for Mental Culture, but as far as she had been able to discover, by turning the Specimen over under the Microscope, there was nothing Vicious in his make-up. He was simply a Case of Atrophied Cerebellum and Ingrowing Nerve.

Clarence could not get next to all the Long Words or he

would have felt all cut up about it. As it was, he decided not to correspond, even after learning her Name.

Moral: *Many a Man is up against an Analysis when he is trying to make a Paralysis*

The Fable of the One Who Got What Was Coming to Him and then Some More

Once there was a Man who bought his Pleasures by the Pound. He was a Close Buyer. At any time that he unwound the Shoe-String and disgorged a One-Case Note, he was expecting to get a Return of about $1.60 or else he considered himself Stung. His Family Motto was "Get your Money's Worth."

At a Hotel he would keep the Lights turned on all night so as to Catch Even on his Bill. Sometimes on the Trolley-Car he would ride two Blocks past his own House and then walk back, because he wanted to get as much as possible for his Five Cents. Once he was beguiled into paying Five for a Ticket to a Charity Ball. Rather than to be out the Five he danced from 10 p.m. to 4 a.m. He was the Man who insisted on the Third Encore at the Theatre and howled for a Baker's Dozen every time he bought Eggs.

Whenever he got Enlargement of the Heart and began to spend Money on himself, he expected every one to pay lots of Attention to him. Once he hired a Cab by the Hour. He was sitting in a Cozy Corner, slowly fighting his way to the bottom of a High Ball, when a Policeman came in and told him that the Cabman was freezing to death outside.

"That's all right," was the Reply. "He's getting paid for it."

By the time he got through with a Free Lunch there was nothing left except Olives.

One Day on the Train he wanted a Snack, but he did not feel Hungry a Dollar's Worth. He hated to go into a Diner and get away with only Eighty-five Cents' worth of Provender. So he decided to make a Supreme Effort to stick the Company. He began with Blue-Points and Soup and Fish, and then he was horrified to find that he had Enough. But he was cinched for a Dollar, so he ordered Ribs of Beef, half a Duck, seven Vegetables, Ice-Cream, Pie, Cheese, and a Large Coffee. When he arrived at his Destination he was in the Baggage-Car ahead. His Last Words had been, "Make the Company pay all Expenses."

Moral: *No one loses out in the Dining-Car except the Stockholders.*

The Fable of the Girl Who Wanted to Warm Up When It Was Too Late

Once there was a good Young Man who delivered Milk and sang in the Choir. He allowed his Affections to get all snarled up with a tall female Elfin named Sophy. Fate kissed him off and he lay froze against the Cushion. It appeared that Sophy had no time for him, because he was about two Notches below her in the Social Scale. Sophy's father was an Auctioneer and Agent for a Patent Churn.

The Young Man, whose Name was Otis, removed the Gaff from his quivering Bosom and began to lay Plans to humble her Pride. After placing his Milk Route in the Hands of a Reliable Agent, he went up to the City and began to take Lessons on the Horn. He practised until he was able to crawl inside of a big Oom-Pah and eat all of the Low Notes in the Blue Book. The Hard Part of a Sousa March was Pie for him. He could close his Eyes and run up the Scale, and then down again until he struck the Newfoundland Growl coming at the end of "Rocked in the Cradle."

Then he went back and joined the Silver Cornet Band. On Decoration Day he was up at the Head of the Line, just behind the Grand Marshal with the Red Sash, and he carried a Tuby that looked like the Entrance to a Cave. His Uniform was fancy enough for a Colonel on the Governor's Staff.

When he swept down Main Street scaring all the Horses and causing the Window-Panes to rattle, every one along the Line of March who knew Ote was proud of himself.

Sophy saw him and got ready to do a little Hedging. After the Parade, when he was in the Bon-Ton Candy Kitchen, with a Handkerchief around his Neck, ordering up Strawberry Soda, then Sophy broke through the Circle of Admirers and bade him Welcome. Otis gave her a cruel Look and pretended that he did not remember her Name.

That Evening she saw him pass the House three times with the Tuby on one Arm and a red-headed Milliner on the other.

Moral: *Adversity often hatches out the true Nobility of Character.*

The Fable of What Our Public Schools and the Primary System Did for a Poor but Ambitious Youth

Once there were two Boys growing up in a large City. One had been born with a Silver Spoon in his Mouth. At that time Silver was regarded as a valuable Metal.

The other Boy had no Assets to speak of, but he had very wisely chosen to be born under the Stars and Stripes, where the Poor Boy with a gnawing Ambition gets every Show for his White Alley.

This Urchin was named Jimmy, and even at the age of six he was looking forward to the Time when he would be big enough to kill a Policeman.

Jimmy resided with his Parents in a bummy little one-story Shack. He went barefoot every Year as soon as the Frost got out of the Ground, and his favorite Stamping-Ground was the Railway Yards. One of the Joys of his Childhood was to get together a Gang of Hicks and throw Stones at the

Brakeman. He was a member of a tough Ball Team and knew how to play Seven-Up.

Across the Street from where Jimmy lived there was a magnificent Brick House with a Mansard Roof.

Within this Palace dwelt a Boy who had been handicapped with the Name of F. Lawrence. However, it was hoped that his Money would carry him through. F. Lawrence had been warned against Jimmy. His Mamma often took him on her Knee and told him how one of his Ancestors turned the Water into Long Island Sound, and that it was his Duty to guard the Family Name and not speak to People who worked by the Day.

So F. Lawrence would stand at the Window and make Faces at Jimmy outside. Whereupon Jimmy would double-dare him to come into the Street; but F. Lawrence remembered about the Family Name and refused to associate with any low-born Characters. But when he went out to take his Dancing Lesson, Jimmy would chase him a few Blocks and call him Names that were almost as bad as F. Lawrence.

Jimmy had a Proud Nature, even if his Old Man did work at the Gas-House. The Taunts and Insults heaped upon him by the Young Aristocrat caused him many Bitter Reflections, but likewise it awoke in him a Stern Resolve that some day or other he would make F. Lawrence look like a Yellow Clarionet.

"I have neither Wealth nor Social Station," Jimmy would say to himself, "but I have Youth and Strength and a cast-iron Nerve, and if they expect to keep me down they will have to tie me."

While F. Lawrence was away at the 'Varsity learning Sanscrit and how to Inhale without choking himself, humble Jimmy was circulating in the Ward, learning the Duties of Citizenship. He developed a Right Swing that was calculated to put somebody out of the Business. It was a common saying among his Admirers that you could not dent Jimmy with an Axe. And yet, only a few Years before, he had been a bare-footed Cub stealing Rides on the Freight-Trains.

He was in Demand at all Primary Elections. Whenever he wanted to be a Delegate or something, his Name went on the Ticket or else there was an Ambulance Call. One Spring, while F. Lawrence was down on the Riviera trying to conceal the Fact that he had been born in America, Jimmy stacked the Cards on the Pious Element and was elected Alderman.

His real Career now opened up. He gathered about him all the Local Statesmen who were not on Earth for their Health. Whenever an Ordinance came up, they held it over a few Weeks until they could Investigate and make sure that the Taxpayers were being Protected.

Jimmy acquired a Reputation as a Philanthropist and Friend of the Poor. Every time a down-trodden Porch-Climber was taken in by those Enemies of Society who wear the Blue Clothes, Jimmy would go around and fix up the Bail Bond, and explain to the Judge that his Friend was a Working-Boy with a Mother dependent on him. By such unselfish Acts as these he perfected a Private Machine and had on his Staff a great many useful Workers who said that they were willing to come to the Front at any time and do anything for him, up to and including Murder.

Jimmy had started out with no Pull or Prestige. He had nothing to carry him through except his Character. And now, at the age of forty-two, he was the Uncrowned King of the Slate-Makers, the Main Blazotts, and the acknowledged Boss.

As a Boy, his entire Wardrobe stood him about Eighty Cents. Now, his Jewels alone figured up $1400 and his Clothes had Silk lining. He owned a Buffet in which he had to use four Men behind the Bar, and sometimes the Slot Machines alone gave him a Rake-Off of $50 a Day.

And how about F. Lawrence, the pampered Patrician who had been wont to jeer at the Poor Boy and treat him with Contempt? He had been leading a Life of Idleness and Luxury, instead of getting out and hustling for the Taxpayer and Working-Man. But his Pride was due to get a hard Fall. Humble Jimmy, the Gas-House Boy, had a lovely Dose of Poetic Justice all fixed up for F. Lawrence.

It appears that F. Lawrence, after the Death of his Father, succeeded to the Presidency of a Corporation organized to trim the Public. This Corporation needed a Renewal of the Franchise. It had to get the Renewal or put up the Green Blinds, and that is why F. Lawrence got busy.

Every one told him that he would have to see Jimmy. There would be nothing doing until Jimmy had been Seen and seen Proper. And that is how it came about that the haughty Magnate, who once reviled the ragged Urchin, came with his Hat in his Hand and began to Crawl as soon as he struck the Front Door.

Here was a Grand Opening for Jimmy. He had the Chance of his Life to hand out a Hunk of Retribution by saying: "When I was a penniless Lad you mocked my Poverty. Now I am Well-Off and Powerful and you come to Square yourself. Go!"

Jimmy did nothing of the Sort. Large Natures, such as his, are not capable of a Petty Revenge. He was Magnanimous. He seized F. Lawrence by the Undressed Kid and led him to the Back Room.

As soon as he became assured that the Taxpayers were not going to get the Nub End of the Deal, he agreed to deliver the Goods.

Then he made some Inquiries about the Corporation, and it seemed to be such a fair and above-board Proposition that he took many shares of Stock.

To-day he is one of the Directors and sits at the same Mahogany Table with F. Lawrence, showing what a Poor Boy may accomplish in this Country if he leaves Liquor alone and does not waste his Time.

Moral: *If shy on the Family Name, pay some Attention to the Pull.*

The Joys of Single Blessedness

The bachelor is held up to contempt because he has evaded the draft. He is a slacker. He has side-stepped a plain duty. If he lives in the small town he is fifty percent. joke and fifty percent. object of pity. If he lives in a city, he can hide away with others of his kind, and find courage in numbers; but even in the crowded metropolis he has the hunted look of one who knows that the world knows something about him. He is led to believe that babies mistrust him. Young wives begin to warn their husbands when his name is mentioned. He is a chicken hawk in a world that was intended for turtle doves. It is always taken for granted that the bachelor *could* have married. Of course, he might not have netted the one he wanted first off. It is possible that, later on, circumstances denied him the privilege of selection. *But* it is always assumed by critics of the selfish tribe, that any bachelor who has enough money in the bank to furnish a home, can, if he is persistent, hound some woman into taking a chance.

Undoubtedly the critics are right. When we review the vast army of variegated males who have achieved matrimony, it seems useless to deny that the trick can be turned by any man who is physically capable of standing up in front of a preacher or whose mental equipment enables him to decide that he should go into the house when it rains.

If Brigham Young, wearing throat whiskers, could assemble between thirty-five and forty at one time, how pitiful becomes the alibi of the modern maverick that he never has managed to arrive at any sort of arrangement with a solitary one!

We know that women will accept men who wear arctic overshoes. Statistics prove that ninety-eight percent. of all those you see on station platforms, wearing "elastics" on their shirtsleeves, have wives at home.

The whole defense of bachelorhood falls on the ground

when confronted by the evidence which any one may accumulate while walking through a residence district. He will see dozens of porch-broken husbands who never would have progressed to the married state if all the necessary processes had not been elementary to begin with, and further simplified by custom.

Even after he is convinced, he will stubbornly contend as follows: "Possibly I am a coward, but I refuse to admit that all these other birds are heroes."

At least, he will be ready to confess that any one can get married at any time, provided the party of the second part is no more fastidious and choosey than he is.

These facts being generally accepted, the presumption of guilt attaches to every single man beyond the age of thirty. And if, as the years ripen, he garners many dollars, and keeps them in a hiding place which is woman-proof, he slowly slumps in public esteem until he becomes classified with those granite-faced criminals who loot orphan asylums or steal candlesticks from an altar.

Finally he arrives at a state of ostracized isolation. He has every inducement to be utterly miserable, and probably would be so, except for frequent conversations with married men.

At this point we get very near to the weakest point in the general indictment against bachelors: Is it generally known that bachelors privately receive encouragement and approbation from married men?

Not from all married men, it is true. Not, for instance, from the husband of any woman who happens to read these lines. But they *do* receive assurances from married men, of the more undeserving varieties, that matrimony is not always a long promenade through a rose bower drenched with sunshine. The word "lucky" is frequently applied to single men by the associate poker players who are happily married.

The difficulty in rescuing the hardened cases of bachelorhood is that the unregenerate are all the time receiving private signals from those supposed to be saved, to lay off and beat it, and escape while the escaping is good. Many of them would have fallen long ago except for these warnings.

There are times when the most confirmed, cynical, and self-centred celibate, influenced by untoward circumstances and unfavourable atmospheric conditions, believes that he could be rapturously content as a married man, and that he is cheating some good woman out of her destiny. Conversely, the Darby who wants the world to know that his Joan is a jewel and his children are intellectual prodigies and perfect physical specimens—even this paragon, who would shudder at mention of a divorce court, tells his most masonic friends that it must be great to have your freedom and to do as you darn please.

No matter which fork of the road you take, you will wonder, later on, if the scenery on the other route isn't more attractive.

The bachelor, being merely a representative unit of weak mankind, isn't essentially different from the Benedict. Probably at some time or other he wanted to get married and couldn't. Whereas, the married one didn't want to get married and was mesmerized into it by a combination of full moon, guitar music, and roly-boly eyes.

A poor wretch who had lived under the stigma of bachelorhood for years once confided to several of us that he was all ready to be married at Columbus, Ohio, in 1892, and then learned that it would cost at least eight dollars to put the thing over.

Bachelors are willing to be segregated or even separately taxed, but they don't wish to be branded with too hot an iron. They come to regard themselves as potential married men who never received notice of their inheritances. Married men are merely bachelors who weakened under the strain. Every time a bachelor sees a man with an alpaca coat pushing a perambulator, he says, "There, but for the grace of God, goes me!"

Whatever excuses the bachelor may secrete in his own

mind, the following definite counts have been drawn against him:

1st. It is the duty of every good man to become the founder of a home, because the home (and not the stag boarding-house) is the corner-stone of an orderly civilization.

2d. It is the duty of every high-minded citizen to approve publicly the sacrament of marriage, because legalized matrimony is the harbour of safety. When the bachelor ignores the sacrament, his example becomes an endorsement of the advantages offered to travellers by that famous old highway known as "The Primrose Path."

3d. It is the duty of every student of history and economics to help perpetuate the species and protect the birth rate.

These are the damning accusations. Any representative woman's club, anywhere, would bring in a verdict of "guilty" against a notorious bachelor, in two minutes, without listening to witnesses.

The moment a man marries, the indictment is quashed. For the time being, he is snow white. A little later, after the divorce proceedings, he may become speckled, but he never sinks quite back to the degraded estate of bachelorhood.

He tried to be a good citizen.

Having an altruistic and almost Chautauquan regard for home and the marriage sacrament, and feeling that *someone* had to step forward and save the birth rate, he put aside all considerations of personal convenience and, like a sun-kissed hero, stepped to the edge and jumped over the precipice.

Yes, he did! You know he did!

Here is what happened:

The dear old goof found himself in immediate juxtaposition to The Most Wonderful Woman in All the World. When she smiled at him, his blood pressure went up twenty points. When she appeared to forget that he was among those present, he wanted to rush into the street and lie down in front of a taxicab. He hovered near her, every night, until ordered out. Then he reeled back to his den, stepping from one cloud to another. He sat up in the still hours of the morning to write notes which elected him even if, later on, he had wanted to welch. He arrived at his office without remembering what had happened since he left home. He tried to dictate letters, and nothing came from him except gurgles. He wondered what was happening to Her. In the telephone booth—only about eight cubic feet of air—partial asphyxiation after twenty minutes. But who wouldn't be willing to die, with the sound of that Voice strumming in the ears, like an Æolean harp hanging in the gateway of Paradise?

Now, when Waldo finally got married, does any one really insist that he did it because he was prompted by a sense of his duty to provide food and lodging for a member of the opposite sex?

Did he calmly decide to give his endorsement to the sacrament of marriage and to help protect the birth rate?

Did he?

Lay the bride's curse on the bachelor, if you will, and let his name become a byword and hissing at every bridge party, but don't hang any medals on Waldo until you have all the facts in his case—which will prove to be a carbon copy of a million other cases.

Waldo got married because he needed sleep. It was a toss-up between Sweeties and a sanitarium, and he selected the easier way.

He could not picture an existence which did not include the radio-magnetic presence of Honey. He was governed by sex impulse and not by what he had read in books on sociology.

Not until weeks later, emerging from the honeymoon trance, did he discover that he had honorably discharged his obligations to Society and had become a member of the Matrimonial Legion of Honor.

What happened to Waldo might have happened to any petrified hermit now hiding at a club. And if Waldo, on a certain occasion, had happened to meet merely Another Flapper, instead of The Most Wonderful Woman in the

World, he might now be camped at a hotel instead of being assistant manager of a nursery.

We are all wisps, and the winds of chance blow in many directions.

Just because a man gets married is no sign that he has a high and holy and abiding regard for womanhood. Visit any court room and hear the sufferer go into detail: He threw a meat platter at her—squeezed her arm until it was black and blue—tore the feathers off her new hat—kicked the Pomeranian into the fireplace—made her sleep on the lounge, etc., etc., etc.

It isn't usually a lack of intense regard and reverence for womanhood that keeps the bachelor single. Often enough, it is a lack of regard for himself as a fit companion for the goddess up there above him on the pedestal.

One of the most highly despised bachelors I ever knew once said that if he ever asked a woman to marry him and she said, "Yes," he'd begin to have his suspicions of her. And yet he was supposed to be a woman-hater!

The rooming-houses are packed with mature single men, each of whom looks up to Class A women with such worshipful adoration that he never has felt worthy of possessing one of the angelic creatures.

Charley Fresh—who regards himself as the irresistible captivator—googles his way among the girls for six nights a week and is known as a "lady's man." The marooned and isolated males who watch his performance refuse to enter into any contest which features Charley Fresh as a formidable rival. If he is what the women want, they cannot qualify. They accept the inevitable, and decide that by habit and circumstances they are debarred from the matrimonial raffle, and they might as well make the best of it. They know that they lack the peacock qualities of the heartbreaker, as they have studied him in Robert W. Chambers and the movies. They never could live up to the specifications. Not one of them wants to compromise by grabbing a third-rater. They want a topnotcher, or nothing; and they haven't the financial rating, the parlor training, the glib vocabulary, the baby-blue eyes, the curly hair and the athletic shoulders to make them real mates for the distant Dianas of their day dreams.

Some are restrained by caution, some by diffidence, and some are put out of the running by Fate.

Is it not true that the bachelor uncle is always a hot favorite with the children? And doesn't he often tell Minnie, his brother's wife, that he would give a thousand shares of Steel Common if he could have one of his own? Of course, if he had one he wouldn't know what to do with it; but it just shows that the parental instinct can often be aroused by a good home-cooked dinner.

This defense of bachelors is getting to be pretty wobbly; but it still has a few guns in reserve. For instance, if the birth rate languishes, shall no part of the blame be put on the modernized young woman who is ring-shy until he can show her a five-thousand-dollar automobile?

How about the great armies of salaried women who have come into financial independence in the office buildings and don't wish to exchange it for the secluded dependence of the flat buildings?

There are oodles of reasons why the bachelors have not married. Let there be general rejoicing that many of them have remained single. Special congratulations to the might-have-been children! They will never know what they have escaped.

Who knows but your old friend Bill was made a bachelor by Divine decree, so that some poor, frail woman wouldn't have to sit up until two or three o'clock every morning?

And now for some pointed advice and inside information: If you believe that grown-up males who refuse to marry are, in the aggregate, a menace to society, don't base your propaganda on the assumption that bachelors live in a care-free Paradise, which they are loath to exchange for the harrowing responsibilities of the family circle. Try to convince the bridegroom that he is winning a prize instead of surrendering a birth-right.

If you want to keep a line waiting at the marriage license window, preach to the wandering sheep that they should come in from the bleak hills, and gambol in the clover pastures of connubial felicity.

Arrange with the editors to suppress all detailed reports of divorce trials; also to blue-pencil the shoddy jokes which deal with mothers-in-law and rolling pins.

Fix it with theatrical producers so that the stage bachelor will not be a picturesque hero, just a trifle gray about the temples, who carries a packet of dried rose leaves next to his heart, while the husband is a pale crumpet who is always trembling and saying, "Yes, my dear."

Try to induce department stores to remove those terrifying price tags from things worn by women. Many a wavering bachelor has looked in a show window and found, by an easy mental calculation, that his full salary for one month would supply My Lady with sufficient wardrobe to take her past the morning tub, but not enough to carry her into the street.

The two lone items of hats and shoes would spell bankruptcy to a fellow of ordinary means, and he knows that there must be countless other intermediate items connecting up the $60 hats with the $22 shoes.

At least, give him credit for always picturing *his* phantom wife as being extremely well dressed. Married men may be tight with the checkbook and moan over the bills; but the intangible, make-believe wife of the secluded bachelor always wears the most *chic* and alluring confections shown by the shops.

He has no intention of giving up the two-room snuggery which has been his home for eight years, but if he *should* become adventurous at any time and go sailing the uncharted seas, he knows that his travelling companion will be a queen in royal garb. She will sit in the rear of the boat, bedecked with pearls and wearing a coronet. He never meets her, but his intentions are generous, up to the last.

"I wouldn't get hooked up unless I could give my wife the best of everything." How often have we heard those words, spoken by some brave outlaw. The inference being that he has passed up a sacred privilege for fear that he could not supply Her with all of the costly luxuries she deserved.

Whereas, his associates know that he has become encased with a hard crust of habits and could never adapt himself to the give-and-take conditions of married life.

They can't be taught new tricks after they begin to moult.

But they continue to explain, and even in the deepest recesses of the most funereal reading-room of the most masculine club, you cannot find one so fussy and crabbed but that he will insist that he is "fond of children."

The lexicon of the unyoked is full of Old Stuff. The most hopeless misogynist (see dictionary) can always hang the blame on someone else and give himself a clean bill.

The point now being made is that the information agencies, by which the credulous public is influenced, seem to aid and abet the bachelors. Newspapers, magazines, picture plays, novels, current anecdotes—all have fallen into the easy habit of making it appear that the bachelor is a devil of a fellow; that the spirit of youth abides with him after it has deserted the stoop-shouldered slaves commonly depicted as mowing lawns or feeding furnaces.

The bachelor, as an individual, may sell very low in his immediate precinct; but the bachelor, as a type, has become fictionized into a fascinating combination of Romeo and Mephistopheles.

You never saw a bachelor apartment on the stage that was not luxurious and inviting. Always there is a man servant: It is midnight in Gerald Heathcote's princely lodgings. Gerald returns from the club. Evening clothes? Absolutely!

He sends Wilkins away and lights a cigarette. There is a brief silence, with Gerald sitting so that the fireplace has a chance to spotlight him. It is a bachelor's apartment and midnight. Which means that the dirty work is about to begin.

If, at any time, you are sitting so far back in a theater that you cannot get the words, and you see a distinguished figure of a man come on R. U. E., self-possessed, debonair, patronizing—no need to look at the bill. He is a bachelor, and the most beautiful lady in the cast is all snarled up in an "affair" with him. If she ever crosses the threshold of his voluptous "lodgings," unaccompanied by a private detective or a chaperon, her reputation won't be worth a rusty nickel.

That's the kind of a reputation to have! Never too old to be wicked! Lock up the débutantes—here come the bachelors!

Now, if you persistently represent single blessedness as seated in a huge leather chair, with Wilkins bringing whisky and soda, and a married woman of incredible attractiveness waiting to call him up on the 'phone, you need not be surprised if, in time, the whole social organization is permeated with a grotesque misconception of the true status of the bachelor.

For years I have been compelled to observe large flocks of him at close range. Only about one half of one per cent. have lodgings which could be used effectively for a Belasco setting. Only a very few, mostly east of Buffalo, employ English manservants to "do" for them. Those who like to refer to "my man" are compelled to get new ones every few weeks. Probably the lonesomest job in the world, next to taking care of a lighthouse, is to valet an unmarried man who has gone in for dancing.

Bachelors do not habitually wear evening clothes. To get one of them into the extreme regalia may involve the use of chloroform. Nearly every bachelor knows a few married women; but these women are not pursuing him—that is, not all of the time. Once in a while they pursue him in order to find out what has become of their husbands.

If one of these charming matrons visited a bachelor apartment, it would be to throw a bomb. She has him down on her list as poison ivy.

The bachelor is a polite outcast, and he knows it. The married folks tell stories about him, and it is all for the best that he never hears them. For instance: "I helped him off with his overcoat when he came in. We wondered why he didn't follow us into the living-room. I went back and found him standing in the hallway. Yes, indeed, waiting for his check! When the children came in to meet him, he trembled like a leaf—thought they were going to kiss him. When he sat down for dinner he inspected the knife and then wiped the plate with his napkin. After dinner the maid found a quarter on the tablecloth."

The idealized bachelor of fiction may be a super-gallant, but the real article is a scared fish the moment he swims out of his own puddle.

Possibly you expected from me a wordy attempt to prove that a man may acquire happiness by avoiding matrimony. Well, you cannot secure contentment by a mere avoidance of anything. The only worth-while days are those on which you sell a part of yourself to the brotherhood of man and go to the mattress at night knowing that you have rendered service to some of the fellow travellers. The more you camp by yourself the more you shrivel. The curse and the risk of bachelorhood is the tendency to build all plans around the mere comforts and indulgences of the first person singular.

Sometimes a bachelor gets to taking such good care of himself that he forgets that some day or other he will need six friends to act as pallbearers.

Next to solitaire, probably the most interesting single-handed pastime is trying to visualize one's own funeral. The bachelor often wonders if it will be an impressive function.

No use talking, when a transient undertakes the journey alone, he is compelled to be in doubt as to terminal facilities. His friendships are insecure and all the arrangements unstable. He has a lot of liberty, but he doesn't know what to do with it.

No man can cheat the game by merely hiding in a hotel and having his meals served in his room.

He can run in the opposite direction from matrimony until he is all out of breath, but he will never travel far enough to get away from himself. When he flees from the responsibilities of family life he is incidentally leaving behind him many of the experiences which belong to a normal career. He cannot get away from the double-entry system of accounts revealed in Doctor Emerson's essay on Compensation. The books must balance.

No man can take twelve months' vacation each year. A vacation is no fun except when it comes as a release from the regular routine. Each July the married man is supposed to sing:

"My wife's gone to the country. Hurrah! Hurrah!"

Thereby he gets an edge on the bachelor. He has a chance to throw his hat in the air at least once a year. When does the bachelor pull his "Hurrahs"? Think it over.

If the locked-up hubbies believe that the boys still at large are raising Cain seven nights a week and fifty-two weeks in the year, let them cease to be envious. It can't be done. The most fatiguing activity in the world is that of roystering. It is terrible to be fed up on roystering. Almost any group of case-hardened bachelors would rather row a boat than sit around a table and sing.

Bachelors do not regard their respective caves and caverns as modified cabarets. Their so-called home life is merely a recognition of the physical fact that no one can entirely dispense with slumber.

The "jolly bachelor" in his own retreat is often just as jolly as a festoon of crape. He is not discontented. He is calmly reconciled. But not celebrating.

He has been saved from the shipwreck by miraculous intervention, but he finds himself on a lonely island and not a sail in sight.

The bachelor doesn't have to watch the clock, and no one is waiting to ask him where he has been; but how about that rapidly approaching day when he will not find—in all the world—ham and eggs that are cooked just right or coffee fit to drink?

As the autumn days grow shorter, and each milestone begins to look more like a tombstone, the bachelor becomes less and less declamatory regarding the joys of single blessedness.

He doesn't weaken, mind you. He can explain why it would have been manifestly impossible for him, at any time, to undertake such a crazy experiment. His training, his temperament, the conditions enforced by his employment, the uncertainty of his financial outlook—these and thirty other good reasons made it utterly impossible for him even to think of playing such a ghastly joke on a nice woman.

He is there with a defense; but when you ask him to add up the net blessings and benefits which accrue to the bachelor, his discourse becomes diffuse and unconvincing. If he is past forty, he doesn't brag at all. If he is past fifty, he begins to talk about the weather.

And now, having received all of this secret information from the camp of the enemy, you know as much as we do regarding the joys of single blessedness.

Musical Comedy

When the first piano was built the owner needed something to put on top of the piano, so the popular song and the light opera were invented. As the musical taste of succeeding buyers developed and improved, light opera became lighter and lighter until at last they had to weight it down to keep it on the piano. There came a time when the manufacturers were prohibited under the Pure Food Law from using the opera label. They had to call the output something or other, so they compromised on "musical comedy."

Musical comedy has done a great deal for our fair land. It has depopulated the laundries, reduced the swollen fortunes of Pittsburgh, and bridged the social chasm between the honest working girl and the pallid offspring of the captain of industry.

It has taught William Shakespeare how to take a joke. It has developed a colony of angels and incidentally it has given the foot-power piano an excuse for being.

A good musical comedy consists largely of disorderly conduct occasionally interrupted by talk. The man who provides the interruptions is called the librettist. I would advise any man who hasn't the nerve to be a foot-pad or is too large to get through a transom, to become a librettist.

I'd rather be a burglar than the man who writes the book,
For the burglar is anonymous—a self-concealing crook;
When they catch *him* with the goods he merely does a term in jail,
While the author has to stand and take a roast from Alan Dale.

I wrote this years ago, but it is still true.

The so-called music of musical comedy must be the kind that any messenger boy can learn to whistle after hearing it twice. At the same time it must satisfy the tall-browed critic who was brought up on Tschaikowski and Bach. As for the dialogue, it must be guaranteed to wring boisterous laughter from the three-dollar patron who has a facial angle of thirty degrees, and a cerebellum about the size of an olive; also it must have sufficient literary quality and subtle humor to please the dead-head who is sitting in the fourth row with a hammer in one hand and a javelin in the other.

Every young man who goes into the libretto business thinks he is going to revolutionize the American stage. He is going to begin where W. S. Gilbert left off. He gets a fountain pen, a pad of paper, and a few pounds of opiate, and then he dreams it all out. He is going to write a musical play with a consistent and closely connected plot, an abundance of sprightly humor and nothing said or done that would bring the blush of shame to the cheek of the most sensitive manager.

His getaway is usually very promising. By the way of novelty he has an opening chorus. A lot of people are standing around in aimless groups there in the green sunshine. Occasionally the green sunshine changes to amber. They tell all about themselves and explain their emotions. Then the principals begin coming on and tell why *they* are present, and the wedding is announced and the people in front begin to get a faint outline of plot. This goes on for about ten minutes until a beautiful blonde, who was educated for grand opera and then changed her mind, suddenly says, apropos of nothing in particular. "Oh, I am so happy to-day I could sing my favorite song, 'Won't you be my little gum-drop?' "

That is what is known as a "music cue." That is where the author goes into the side pocket and the producer becomes the whole proposition.

First the beautiful blonde sings it all by herself. Then the beautiful tenor with talcum powder all over his face comes out and helps her. Then the refined comedian, recently graduated from vaudeville, breaks in and they do the gum-drop number as a trio. The soubrette arrives, merely by accident, and the song regarding the gum-drop now becomes a quartette. Then eight young ladies in Spanish costumes come out and sing it, introducing a dance. Then eight young ladies in white are lowered from the flies and they sing it while hanging in the air. Then the lights are turned out and the entire company sings it in the moolight. Then the sunshine is turned on again and all sing it by daylight.

The man who leads the orchestra is a mind-reader. He knows that the public wants more verses of the gum-drop song whether it applauds or not. This is what is known as the "noiseless encore." The reason he is so willing to respond to encores is that he wrote the song.

At last, after the entire company has sung and danced itself into a state of staggering exhaustion, and even the iron-handed ushers have become satiated, the whole covey disappears and that grand old annoyance who shows up in every musical play, the bride's father, wanders on the stage and tries to collect the shattered fragments of plot. Of course nobody pays any attention to him. All the people in front are lying back limp and groggy, trying to recover from the excitement of that gum-drop affair. They have forgotten all about the fragment of "story" that showed up a half hour before. Father, however, starts in to remind the audience of the wedding day and the bride and the birth-mark and the picture in the locket and the other essentials, and just about the time he is getting a foothold the Egyptian dancers glide on and everything is once more floating upside down in the air. The morning newspapers say that the plot did not seem to be well sustained.

I do not wish to be understood as attacking musical comedy. It has helped a great many people who belong in trolley cars to ride in motor cars. It provides mental relaxation for the tired business man who doesn't want to think. Probably if he ever stopped to think, he would get up and go out.

Musical comedy has educated the public. When it was first introduced the American people were devoted to such simple and old-fashioned melodies as "Roll On, Silvery Moon," "Then You'll Remember Me," "When the Corn is Waving, Annie, Dear," and "The Gypsy's Warning." The campaign of education has been going on for years and now we have worked up to a midnight show on a roof, with songs which would be suppressed by the police if the police could fathom the significance of the *double entendre*.

It is said that every man in the world thinks he can edit a newspaper, manage a hotel and write a comic opera. I have been in the newspaper business and I have gone against operas that were trying to be comic. I am still sure that I can manage a hotel.

The Tortures of Touring

Some people think that the first purpose of motoring is not to travel but to arrive. The driver who carries his helpless victims from Buffalo to Albany in one day goes about accepting congratulations, whereas he should be hauled into court.

Nothing emitted herewith must be regarded as a narrow-minded, pedestrian protest against motoring in general. The joys of life may be made to increase with the multiplication of cylinders. The privilege of cutting across country and the diversion of travel from stiff and straight rail lines to shady by-ways—these are real boons.

Attack is being made only on those motorists who are obsessed with the belief that because a car *can* hit up fifty-five an hour, it is hanging back when it goes a measly thirty-five, and who further count up the result of their tours by the miles instead of by the smiles.

The main idea with the road-whippets seems to be the necessity of registering at some far distant point within a highly sporting time limit.

Probably the man at the wheel gets most of the zest to be derived from the performance. He feels that exultation which accompanies the controlling and directing of mighty energies. By hanging over the gear he steadies himself physically, and he finds mental employment in repeatedly solving the problem of how to avoid sudden death.

If you like that kind of motoring, by all means claim the privilege of driving. Then, when the car turns turtle, you will have something to hang on to besides a Blue Book.

If you are a back-seat passenger, with a cargo rating the same as that of a suitcase, a thermos bottle, or a golf bag, you will find yourself rock-a-byed through whirling landscapes, and realize all the time that you are merely a limp Something, riding on the winds of Chance.

The driver seems grimly confident that he can always zip within eight inches of the car which comes tearing head on —insanely seeking a collision. How superb of him not to give more roadway than the other fellow gives! And will it be a first-page story, with photographs and the names in black caps? Or will it be bunched with the other casualties of a busy day on the bloody highways?

It seems that the driver himself is never frightened. He is too busy boring a hole in the atmosphere to consider the other people in the car. Their nerves may be kinked into hard knots, and their eyes may be protruding, and their hearts may be suspending action for thirty seconds at a stretch, but what wots it? The delirious chauffeur is having the time of his young life.

Usually, one of the sufferers is the owner of the car. He is simply excess baggage. His only privilege is to produce more money at regular intervals.

Besides, he knows that a classy driver and a high-powered car are both deeply insulted at the very mention of a speed limit. If held down to twenty-five miles an hour, they feel that they have been demoted and had their stripes cut off. They are publicly shamed when they take the dust of cars costing one thousand dollars each, or even less. What is the use of going on the road unless all of the white-faced spectators along the route can be properly impressed?

These must be the facts, because we know that only a few persons, possessed of abnormal cravings, *like* to travel at top speed. Yet the rarest sight in the world is a long-waisted, expensive car moving through a rural district at a sane and safe and sensible pace. It is always trying to arrive at some point, one hundred miles ahead, before six o'clock in the evening.

Among the back-seat victims may be found at least one Invited Guest. When he is asked if he objects to stepping along in high, he supinely answers, "No."

To be auto-shy and favor a moderate gait is evidence of moral inferiority, the same as being seasick or wearing woollen underwear.

Probably persons really alive never come so near to being dead as when they fall out of a motor car at the end of a jolly 200-mile spin.

"Spin" is the word. They know how it feels to be a gyroscope. The blood of each is congealed—partly because he has been visualizing himself as the central attraction of a large funeral. The intellect and the emotions are in a totally benumbed state. Memory is a mere blur of shimmying houses and reeling telephone poles.

The one compensation comes two weeks later when the

sufferer has recovered sufficiently to announce to the envious stay-at-homes that, after taking a late luncheon at Upper Swattomy, he arrived at Manchester in time for dinner.

When a person travels at the speed rate ordained by all high-salaried drivers, he sees nothing much except the roadway. So far as relaxation and instruction and gentle diversion are concerned, he might as well be put into a hollow projectile and fired out of a big Bertha from one city to another.

If he could take a large sleeping powder and lie down in the bottom of the car, after leaving a call, he would be in better condition at the end of the run, because he would not be compelled to put in several hours unspiralling his nerves.

It is well known that the start of a long run is always delayed. Every car that you see burning up the pike is in danger of being late at the next important destination, thereby losing caste.

We spill the golden hours with prodigal foolishness, until we find ourselves in an automobile, and then every minute becomes as precious as a pearl.

There are exclamations of dismay when a sharp detonation tells of tire trouble. Instead of finding it a privilege to get out and stretch the legs and gaze at scenery which consents to stand still, the birds of passage all begin moaning and looking at watches. It is now 4:13 and they expected to be in Springfield at 5:30; but it begins to look as if they might not arrive there until 5:45! Too bad!

Americans are accused of offering too many sacrifices to the mud idol of Aimless Hurry. They never hustle to such small purpose as when they make this mud idol their motor god.

Every day we see them go grinding and flashing past our quiet place in the country. Their faces are tense. They stare straight ahead through the disfiguring goggles. They are half-crouched, to fight more successfully the on-rushing current of air.

They are temporarily ossified—studies in suspended animation. They may be *willing* to turn around and look, but the cervical vertebrae have become locked together and will not rotate. They can see nothing except the white roadway, the speedometer, and the undertaker.

The speed worshippers and schedule slaves have taken the joy out of what should be a restful antidote for brain fag. Motoring would seem to be a proper prescription for nervousness. As a matter of fact the poor neurasthenic who is—or is the victim of—a speed maniac might as well go over to the electric light plant and ride on the flywheel.

Now is the time for an organization of passengers who wish to protect themselves against dare-devil drivers. It should be oath-bound and effective, the same as the Ku Klux Klan. Declaration must be made that the purpose of motor touring is to bring enjoyment to all occupants of the car, even if the driver does earn the contempt of Ralph de Palma and Barney Oldfield.

The maximum rate of speed should be thirty-five miles an hour. The moment the speedometer registers thirty-six, an automatic contrivance should cause a placard to appear on the wind shield immediately in front of the driver. The placard would read as follows: "You are fired."

Or, better yet, have each passenger secrete on his person, before the start, a short leather billy stuffed with sand or bird-shot. This so-called "persuader" is the kind that has been used professionally in all of our large cities since the world was made safe for democracy. Just as the indicator passes the thirty-five-mile mark, each passenger will take a firm grip on the small but dependable weapon and do his duty.

It needs to be understood, once and for all, that even those on the back seats retain their constitutional rights to life, liberty, and the pursuit of happiness.

The driver must watch the roadway; but why should all the others be compelled to help him? When the speed becomes so whistling that the pleasure jaunt resolves itself into a gamble with death, the passengers find themselves gazing straight ahead with a sort of fascinated horror. Mile after mile they discern nothing but a thin white streak, the farther end of which is linked to the horizon.

They should not be compelled to close their eyes and curl their toes in order to avoid going into the ditch.

They should be able to converse among themselves without having their teeth bent inward.

Just as there is no fun in motoring when every new mile becomes another hazardous adventure, so there is no profit in motor travel if too many miles are negotiated each day.

Even when the members of the party are permitted to look at the growing fields and the grazing herds and the comatose villagers on the front porches, they find themselves, after a few hours, definitely filled up with sight-seeing. They are stuffed with impressions.

The average mortal can eat about so much food in twenty-four hours without discomfort. He can listen to so much music and look at so many pictures and read so many pages of a book. By the same token, he can speed only a limited number of miles across country and retain a normal human interest in his surroundings. Let him overtax his capacity, and mental weariness supplements his physical torpor, and he is suffering from what may be designated as *motoritis*.

Therefore let all who have suffered unite in a demand for:

1st: A speed limit of 35 miles an hour.

2d: A distance limit of 100 miles a day.

Anyone not satisfied with the above arrangement may board an express train and lie in a berth.

Automobiles must stop their scooting and learn to tarry.

The occupants of a car should not be compelled to huddle under the lap robes, like hibernating bears, for hours at a time.

All of our motorists, everywhere, are rushing past the things worth seeing, instead of stopping to enjoy them. There is no township, however remote, but has within its boundaries some exhibit which will instruct or entertain the caller.

In order to crowd the one hundred daily miles with rare

entertainment, the thing to do is to stop and visit in every town. You can get acquainted in two minutes.

Don't annoy the postmaster and don't go near the bank. The banker will think that you want a check cashed. Drive right into the heart of Main Street and pull up in front of a red-white-and-blue pole. The barber is the lad for you. He is always sociable, and he can immediately put you in possession of the local traditions and scandals. If there is anything in the whole countryside worth visiting he can give you the needed information, surrounded by details.

Tell him that as you drove in through the residence district, you were more than favorably impressed and that you have stopped off for a visit—and what is there to see? He will immediately submit a list of attractions, which may include the Carnegie Library, a blind pig, and a milch cow that took first prize at the state fair.

Or, better yet, he will ask Elmer to finish the man he is shaving, and he will put on his coat and take you out to meet the town celebrity. It may be the old soldier who gave General Hooker a lot of good advice at Lookout Mountain, or the woman who has been working twenty-two years on a patch quilt which will eventually have seventy-five thousand pieces of silk in it. Or he may want to show you the birthplace of the man who played the slide trombone with Sousa's Band for seven years.

Every incorporated town has some hold upon fame. Here are some sights dug up in smaller Indiana settlements which are entirely overlooked by the tourists:

A town idiot who can foretell the weather and has not made a mistake in five years.

A red-headed negro who drives a pink mule—art eclipsed by nature.

An endless chain whittled out of one piece of wood.

A house which was one of the main stations on the "Underground Railway" for fugitive slaves, before the war.

The quarter-mile track on which Dan Patch received his first try-out as a pacer. First valued at $500 and later, after establishing a world's record, sold for $100,000.

The cream separator first used for making quick apple-jack out of hard cider.

And so on, and so on. Our neglected nation has stored up a wealth of recent legends and is rich in "character types." The way to "See America First" is to resist the silly habit of rushing furiously from one city to another. Seek out the communities in which the residents are severally important as individuals and not mere names in a directory.

Get the habit of stopping and visiting at the slightest provocation. Bestow a little friendly attention on the native population, and it will warm up and begin to radiate hospitality. The city man who is not "stuck up" always makes a sensational hit in the small town. Of course, if you are a metropolitan yap with a movie education and a vaudeville sense of humor and want the "rubes" to perform for your entertainment, you had better keep right on travelling. And ask the local garage man what his charges are before you hire him. When the rural worm turns he gives a correct imitation of a boa constrictor.

In order to insure more leisurely habits of travel and arouse a proper interest in the varied charms of all outlying regions, we need in this country an entirely new sort of guide book for motorists.

The kind of book now in use devotes too much attention to the roadway, instead of giving spicy information about what may be seen from the roadway.

It is a mere chart, whereas it might be made a document bubbling with human interest.

Even when it turns aside to say something about a town on the route, it gives inconsequential facts, such as the population and the altitude above sea level. Even the people who live there do not know how much they are elevated above sea level. And who cares about the population? The question isn't how many people live in the town, but what are they *up* to?

Let us have road guides which will keep the tourists sitting up and interested. Something like the following:

ROUTE 23A—HICKSVILLE TO JUNIPER–26.8M

0.0 Hicksville. Started by Truman Hicks about 1800. The town is famous on account of the Liberty Hotel (large faded structure on Main Street), it being claimed that more travelling men have committed suicide within its walls than in any two other hotels in the state. The elderly persons seen along the business thoroughfares are retired farmers. They are talking about the taxes. The small vacant room next to the post office was used as a manicure parlor for three weeks during 1917, but public sentiment prevailed. In order to get out of town as soon as possible proceed east on Main Street. Note on the left the drug store owned by Henry F. Pilsbry. After local option went into effect, and before the Eighteenth Amendment was passed, Mr. Pilsbry bought two large farms. Look out for stretch of bad pavement. The contractor who did the work was related to the mayor. Cross R. R.

2.6 Bear toward left with County Poor-Farm on right. The old gentlemen with carpet slippers, seated under the trees, thought they could outguess the Board of Trade.

3.3 On a distant hill to right note the spacious farm dwelling owned by Waldo Jefferson, who holds a world's record for being converted, having joined church every winter since 1879.

4.2 Jog left, passing on left country schoolhouse attended in 1874 by Rufus Jinkins, for many years head bartender at the Burnet House, Cincinnati, O.

5.1 Sparrow's Grove. In the general store of Eli Nesbit may be found stick candy dating back to U. S. Grant's first

Administration. Worth a short visit, as it claims the distinction of being the only village in America which does not offer souvenir post cards for sale. Straight on past a fawn-colored bungalow with purple trim to

5.9 Large stock farm owned by Lee J. Truckby, who never took a drink of liquor and has been married four times. He believes in infant damnation and is opposed to hired girls. May be found back of the barn, keeping tab on the help. Visitors just as welcome as the foot and mouth disease.

7.2 Nestling in a grove of jack oaks may be found Zion M. E. Church. Built in the Centennial year. Cupola added in 1888 after a design by the County Superintendent of Schools. The cantata of "Esther" was given at this church during the darkest period of the World War, netting $41 for the Red Cross.

8.4 On the left the Saxby home. There are four Saxby boys, all of whom can move their ears.

9.8 Note at right in pasture a venerable elm tree. It is said that under this tree the Potawatami chiefs, while intoxicated, signed a treaty with Colonel Hoskins, receiving $2 worth of merchandise for all territory lying west of Sandusky.

11.7 Nubbin Hill (Pop. 63). Locally famous as the home of Baz Turnbull, who travelled with a circus for two years. Mr. Turnbull is said to be the only man in the township who still knows where to get it. He is employed at the cream depot and may be easily identified as the one wearing a derby.

13.2 Log cabin back in woods at left, built in 1838 by Jephtha Halliday, father of twelve children. The second oldest son (Cale) moved to Chicago, where he was well known to thousands of people, having officiated for years as train caller at the Illinois Central Station.

16.7 Chautauqua Grove in suburbs of Peatsburg. The tabernacle may be seen in distance. It was in this grove that a member of the Peabody Family of Swiss Bell Ringers became engaged to Professor Herman Belcher, mind-reader and mesmerist. They were married later at Alton, Ill., separating at Crawfordsville, Ind.

16.9 Peatsburg (Pop. 1,500, many residents having been overlooked by the census enumerators, who, in 1920, reported a total of 967). Has more pool players in proportion to size than any other place in the world. Jasper Wilkins, champion checker player of the seventh Congressional District, lives in small frame cottage back of the Harney & Co. Hardware store. Mr. Wilkins is a member of the Volunteer Fire Department. His wife takes in washing. George Spelvin, who may be found in front of post office (cataract over left eye), has been working for 15 years on an invention intended to do away with steel rails in the operation of railway lines. He will exhibit blue-prints to those who can be trusted.

17.3 New iron bridge spans the Catouchie River. Note names of County Commissioners on tablet. All were candidates for reëlection and were defeated.

19.4 Near hitch-rack immediately in front of the Parson farmhouse (bed of nasturtiums in front yard), two citizens of Putnam County engaged in a desperate fist fight in October, 1920, the subject of the controversy being the League of Nations. Said to be the only time when the whole thing was really settled.

20.4 Favorite picnic grounds for Sunday-schools and benevolent orders. Over 1,000 empty pop-bottles picked up during last fiscal year.

22.0 Bennington (Pop. 8). Mr. Klingfeldt, age 93 (brick house with portico), can remember when tomatoes were not supposed to be good to eat.

23.2 Artesian well at right. Water highly impregnated and therefore supposed to have medicinal value. Visited by Irvin Cobb during recent lecture tour.

24.8 Fair grounds at right. On half-mile track Lulu Livingstone in 1908 paced one mile in 2.48 without toeweights. In Floral Hall two years ago was exhibited a rutabaga which bore a striking resemblance to Eben Mosely, president of the Juniper State Bank. It was seen by thousands.

26.8 Juniper (Pop. 3,402). County seat, and known far and wide as "The Pride of Putnam." Has had a cafeteria since 1915 and gets all the Douglas Fairbanks releases within a year after they are seen in large cities. Ellis Trimble, office above the Help-Yourself Grocery, was one of the greatest criminal lawyers in the northern part of the state up to the time they took his liquor away from him. Mae Effingham, a native of the town, is now a member of the Winter Garden chorus. Photographs of Miss Effingham, in costume, may be found in the window of the Applegate Piano and Music Store. Clyde Applegate (the one with the gold in his teeth) can relate many interesting anecdotes dealing with her girlhood back in the old home town.

That is merely a suggestion; it is simply a stray leaf taken from the guide book of the future. But surely, even from this sample, you can begin to sense the possibilities.

Europe has no monopoly on hallowed traditions, and the Wabash has legends the same as the Rhine, if we will just dig them up.

Travel slowly. Stop often. Get under the cover of every neighborhood. Snuggle up until you can feel the very heartbeats of your beloved countrymen. The more you find out about them, the less inclined you will be to pay $2.50 to get into a theatre.